ROYAL COLLEGE OF ART SCHOOLS TECHNOLOGY PROJECT

D&T ROUTES

GRAPHIC PRODUCTS

DESIGN & TECHNOLOGY 14-16

A TC Trust programme sponsored and
supported by the Royal College of Art,
the Esmée Fairbairn Trust,
the Garfield Western Foundation and the
Department for Education and Employment

Hodder & Stoughton

A MEMBER OF THE HODDER HEADLINE GROUP

The writing team

David Perry (Project Director), Louise T Davies (Deputy Project Director), Anthony R Booth (Assistant Project Director), Jim Sage (Assistant Project Director), Doris Massiah (Project Assistant), Alan Booth, Claire Buxton, Mark Hudson, Robin Pellatt, Rob Petrie, Brian Russell, Kalvin Turner (Teacher Fellows), Tricia Collins, Jo Dyer, Terry Fiehn, John Myerson, Tim Perry, Neil Rogers, Kate Sharpe, John West and Ruth Wright.

Acknowledgements

Our special thanks to all the Teacher fellows and their schools, particularly their colleagues, partners, friends and children who have supported them whilst they were writing to meet deadlines.

The Royal College of Art Schools Technology Project wishes to extend its thanks to the following for their help and support in the writing of this book: Kathleen Lund (Chief Executive) and her colleagues at the T.C. Trust, the Department for Education and Employment, Office for Standard in Education (OFSTED), The Royal College of Art and their representatives on the Project Management Group.

Many thanks to the following companies who helped with technical information and photographic material:
AA (Automobile Association), Advertising Standards Authority, Bartle Bogel & Hogarty, BT, Conder Ltd, Susan Curnow, Denford Machine Tools, Dixons PLC, Dräger Oxycrew, Green Moon, Hill & Knowlton, M3D, Philip Harris, Richard Rogers, M&C Saatchi, Southernprint, Superior Creative Services, TechSoft, Thames Water, Unilab, Virgin Atlantic, Webb Scarlett.

The illustrations were drawn by Tony Wilkins, Tony Townsend, Liz Rowe, Bill Donohoe.

The publishers would like to thank the following individuals, institutions and companies for permission to reproduce copyright material in this book. Every effort has been made to trace ownership of copyright. The publishers would be happy to make arrangements with copyright holders whom it has not been possible to contact.

AA (Automobile Association) (57 upper left); Advertising Standards Authority (61); J. Allan Cash (5 top, 6 third upper, 13 top, 30 middle right, 36 left); J. Allan Cash/National Grid (13 bottom); Amnesty International (16 logo); Ancient Art and Architechture Collection (33 left); Avon (15 logo); BAA Technical Library/ICAO (7 top right); Benefits Agency (16 logo); John Birdsall (4 bottom, 5 middle, 6 third lower, 12 bottom two, 22 all, 23 top, 87 bottom left, 88 top right, middle right, 89 top left, middle right, lower right); Gareth Boden (2, 3 upper, 6 right, 8 left, lower, 9 both, 18 middle two, 19 top, 20 both, 21 both, 26 top, middle, 27 middle, lower, 44 lower left, 48 both, 49 both, 50, 53, 58 left lower, 59 right, 65 right, 67 left, 69 all, 70 upper two, 77 upper right, 87 right); Gareth Boden/Artaud Frères (18 lower); Gareth Boden/Stan and Jan Berenstain (3 lower); Gareth Boden/ELC (31 upper); Gareth Boden/Mick Inkpen (72 upper); Gareth Boden/Kall-Kwik (11 top); Braun (15 logo); The Bridgeman Art Library (36 right); British Standards Institute (top left); BT (12 main); Canon (58 lower right); Child Growth Foundation (16 logo); Childline (16 logo); Conder (102); DfEE (12 logo); Denford Machine Tools (71 bottom right, 103 both); Design Council (14 logo); Dixons (23 lower); Dräger (6 left, 15 logo); Early Learning Centre (72 second); Eurostar (14 logo); Halifax (16 logo); Hanson (16 logo); Harrods (15 logo); Hayes Davidson (71 left); Hertz (15 logo); Mark Hudson (77 lower left); ICAO (4 middle); J & S Professional Photography/Jim Lowe (26 bottom, 27 top, 30 left, top right, 32, 33 top right, 35 top left, bottom left, 43 upper left, 44 top, 52 right, 65 left, 66 lower, 80 both, 81, 82 bottom right, 85); J & S Professional Photography/Jim Lowe/Ordnance Survey (57 right); Nadav Kandar (29); Kellogg's (15 logo); Life File/Jeremy Hoare (7 top left); Life File/Emma Lee (7 lower); Life File/Barry Mayes (4 top); Life File/Angela Maynard (6 second); Life File/Aubrey J. Slaughter (7 top middle); Loughborough University (14 logo); The Mail on Sunday (24 top, 25, 56); Marks & Spencer (15 St Michael logo); Military Picture Library (5 bottom); National Blood Service (16 logo); National Power (16 logo); Grant Naylor (70 lower); Oxfam (16 logo); BP plc (55 right); Philip Harris (76 left); M&C Saatchi (55 left); Science Photo Library (83 middle); Shell (16 upper left); Shima Seiki (71 middle right); Southernprint (83 bottom); Superior Creative Services/Richard Masterton (82, left, 90 lower, 91 middle, lower, 92 all); Supertram, Sheffield (15 logo, 57 middle left); TechSoft UK (89 bottom left); Thames Water (17 documents); Thames Water Picture Library (17 bottom right); Thames Water Picture Library/Julian Nieman (17 bottom left); Toppix/Mike Drew (11 middle right, lower right, 24 middle, 54, 86 all); Trip/M. Barlow (11 lower left); John Urling Clark (8 top, 30 bottom, 52 left, 62, 72 lower three, 79 right); John Urling Clark/Power Rangers (31 bottom); Nicky Urling Clark (57 lower left); Virgin Atlantic (58 top); The W.13 Social Club (14 logo); John Walmsley (43 bottom two, 71 top right); Webb Scarlett/Tim Perry (51); Wigmore Hall (14 logo); World International (28)

British Library Cataloguing in Publication Data
A catalogue record for this title is available from The British Library

Student Book
ISBN 0 340 67393 1

First published 1998

Impression number	10	9	8	7	6	5	4	3	2	1
Year			2002	2001	2000	1999	1998			

Teacher's Notes
ISBN 0 340 69736 9

First published 1998

Impression number	10	9	8	7	6	5	4	3	2	1
Year			2002	2001	2000	1999	1998			

Copyright © 1998 Technology Colleges Trust, the Schools Technology Project works under the auspices of the Royal College of Art

Typeset by Wearset, Boldon, Tyne and Wear
Printed in Hong Kong for Hodder & Stoughton Educational, a division of Hodder Headline Plc, 338 Euston Road, London NW1 3BH by Colorcraft Ltd.

Contents

Introduction

This book should be used with the *D&T Routes Core Book* which provides you with advice on how to organise and manage your work in D&T. It will help you to analyse and evaluate products, and help with your designing and manufacturing. It will also increase your understanding of industrial approaches to manufacturing in a variety of materials which both GCSE D&T and GNVQ Manufacturing courses expect.

This book contains:

◆ three **Full Designing and Making Assignments (DMAs)** comprising a design and make challenge together with supporting focused tasks and case studies
◆ five **Outline DMAs** which present you with a design and make Challenge and some starting points to help you get going
◆ **Designing** and **Manufacturing** sections with focused tasks, information and case studies that support your designing and making and increase your knowledge about industrial approaches
◆ a section on **The Business of Manufacturing** which will help to further develop your understanding of manufacturing. This is essential if you are following a GNVQ Manufacturing course but will also enhance your designing and making if you are on a GCSE D&T course.

You can use the DMAs as they stand or to help you to develop your own projects.

There are five focus area books in the *D&T Routes* series: *Resistant Materials*; *Food*; *Textiles*; *Control Products* and **Graphic Products**. You will find it useful to refer to the other books in the series.

Design and Technology produces products in various materials but there are common features in the designing processes and manufacturing processes used. If you are following a GCSE course with a narrower focus you should first think about what is special to your focus area.

What are Graphic Products?

Graphics is about **communication**, particularly through images but also through text and these are frequently used together. **Graphic products**, therefore, are items that use text and images on products which are **functional**. Graphic products often have several functions, only one of which will be to do with communication. For example, a package communicates a great deal about what is inside it (even if it has no text on it), but it also contains and protects what is inside it.

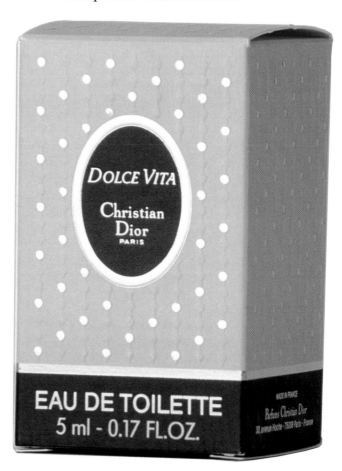

With few words and little obvious imagery, this package communicates messages about luxury very clearly. It is there to make you want it and to protect the bottle inside.

Functional graphic products
can also be fun.

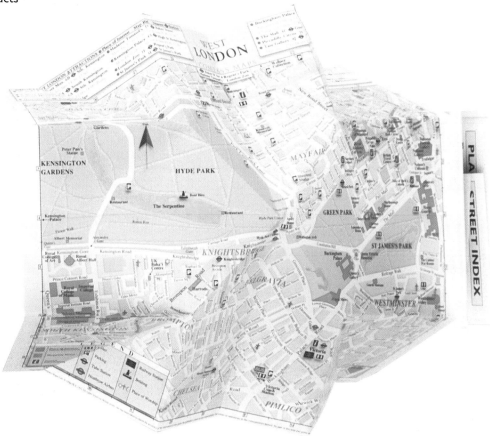

Images 'speak' powerfully to the youngest
child.

Survival

Life can be comfortable – many of us may never have to survive in a life-threatening situation or environment. However, in their sports and leisure pursuits many people put themselves into high-risk situations which test their survival skills.

Unfortunately too many people across the world find themselves in desperate survival situations without any choice. Fortunately, there are many agencies dedicated to supporting human beings in desperate situations.

Well designed graphic products can help people survive many eventualities or help those who rescue or assist them.

Your challenge is to **identify**, **research** and **analyse** a survival situation to lead to you designing a graphic product that will help people survive or support anyone helping them.

Why this challenge is useful

You will learn to research and understand user needs and constraints. You will also learn to analyse situations to find where graphics can provide potential design solutions.

You can design something that is really useful – someone's life may depend on your graphics.

You can **batch produce** your product and have it evaluated by graphics and survival experts.

You may wish to give your idea to an aid agency or emergency service.

Pull out pin
Free hose

Squeeze
levers

Aim at
fire base

FIRE RATING 13A

Values issues

This designing and making activity gives you a special opportunity to think more about values. Surviving often depends on others besides the survivor, and it may help you to think about these questions:

◆ Should people pay for their rescue if they put themselves in potentially dangerous situations, and then need help?
◆ Should all people be treated the same?
◆ How should rescue services be funded?
◆ What about people who are starving to death but help is rejected by their governments?
◆ Should poor countries have to buy essential products (such as butter and meat) when wealthy countries (such as in the EU) throw the same things away?
◆ Should there be an international force to respond to natural disasters? Who should fund it?

To be successful

★ The real success for you will be the satisfaction of designing and making a potentially life-saving graphic product, of help to another human being.
★ Analyse a number of a risk situations very carefully for opportunities for useful graphic products.
★ Your product should communicate well to anyone who might need it.
★ This will be a piece of your assessed coursework. You can increase your chances of exam success by being clear about what the marking scheme expects from you.

How to get going

First of all you must 'get your head round the problem'.

▸ List as many situations as you can where survival is at stake.
▸ Choose some to analyse carefully for the risks involved. What potential exists for graphic products to reduce those risks? (**Note**: your syllabus might restrict the type of graphic product.)
▸ Do you have any survival experiences to relate your work to?
▸ Can you talk to people with experience of real survival situations?

Remember – you will probably need to visit people and places, take photographs, write letters, and wait for replies. All of this is time consuming and needs to be included in your planning.

MINIFLARE 3
DISTRESS SIGNALLING KIT

Graphics on products

For a human being to survive in any situation they need liquid, food, and usually clothing and shelter to protect them from the elements. Any situation may also have special needs.

To improve their situation they and potential helpers will need **special equipment**. For example: medical and rescue equipment; communications systems and products that will make the situation safer straight away.

Analyse the graphics on products used in the survival situations you are considering. Are any of the products predominantly graphic in their purpose? What special needs do graphics in these situations have to fulfil? Do they inform, direct, instruct, warn?

Suggest some ideas for the type of graphic product you might want to make.

 D&T Routes Core Book, Generating ideas, page 53

Making graphic products

If you know of a printing company, or of a large company that does its own in-house printing near your school, try and arrange a visit. Find out what type of graphic products they produce. Find out what facilities your school has.

 D&T Routes Core Book, Collecting information, page 92

It will be useful if you can find out about the production process involved:

- how is the chosen design for a graphic product presented?
- how is a prototype produced?
- how does the printer receive the text and the images?
- what is 'camera ready' artwork?
- what restrictions are there, e.g. on the number of colours?
- what printing methods are used?
- what 'making up' is done?

What resources do you have in your school that can be used to batch-produce graphic products?

 Manufacturing, page 64

Language barriers

The existence of the world market and increasing co-operation between relief and rescue agencies means that survival products are being used in many different countries, by many people who speak different languages.

■ Look on the Internet to find as much information as possible about international standards, symbols and signs.

■ What graphic products do you use that have information for communication to people who speak different languages?

■ Where can you go in this country to see examples of information being communicated to people who speak different languages?
■ How can information, instructions and directions be communicated to deaf and/or blind people?

Graphics that overcome language barriers

Using colour

Colour is vitally important when using graphics. Certain colours imply definite things.

Compile a chart with 3 columns. In the first column make a list of colours. In the second column write what you associate with each colour and in the third, examples of them in use.

Colour	Association	Example	
bright red	danger attention grabbing	red flag – no swimming pillar boxes, the Post Office	
mid grey	BT functional equipment boring	telecom van computer	
orange	warning	worker's jacket traffic light	
deep blue	summer sky	holiday brochure photos	
black	sombre	funeral armband	
bright yellow	sunshine		
white with pastel pink & blue			

▶ **Colour in graphics, page 43**

Pop-ups

Your challenge

Most people are fascinated with pop-up books that combine pictures and stories with different types of movement to provide extra interest.

Pop-ups are a real eye-catcher and a lot of fun. They can also be very successful in clarifying how something looks in three dimensions (3D) for the viewer.

Your challenge is to find out how pop-ups work and to design and make a **high quality** product that uses pop-up techniques for a worthwhile reason.

For example it could be used to advertise a tourist attraction, as a guide to a museum or large department store, or maybe a local business could benefit from 'that something extra!'

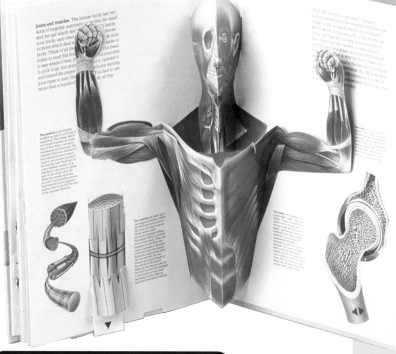

Why this activity is useful

You will learn about methods of cutting, folding and joining paper and card to produce moving parts and 3D structures and how to do this with great accuracy.

You will have to analyse your chosen subject to identify the essential features that represent its character.

You will also practise producing and using precision drawings and models to realise your ideas with minimal wastage of materials.

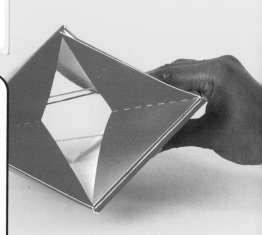

Values issues

◆ There is great concern about the destruction of the world's forests. Many trees are felled to produce the vast amounts of paper-based products world-wide. How can the paper and board industry help to minimise this problem? Would it be better if we used plastic bags instead of paper ones?

◆ How can paper-based products such as maps and guides be designed for the use of blind people?

◆ Pop-up books are very popular with young children. What are the health and safety implications of this?

To be successful

You will need to:

★ make clear the purpose of using pop-up techniques to improve your product

★ be creative, bringing in ideas of your own

★ produce a visually (and dynamically) arresting product

★ design and make parts that join and fit very accurately

★ ensure that your product is well finished and durable

★ use production methods that ensure precision and minimal wastage of materials.

This will be a piece of your assessed coursework. You will increase your chances of success by being clear about what the marking scheme expects from you.

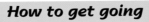

How to get going

▶ Thoroughly investigate existing pop-up products such as cards and books to stimulate your ideas. Collect as many as possible.

▶ Brainstorm in small groups to clarify who your clients and customers could be.

▶ Try out the ideas for modelling the different types of pop-ups – see if you can invent new ones.

▶ Investigate the production methods used in the paper and board industry to produce pop-ups.

▶ Investigate the production methods and equipment that are available to you.

Making pop-ups – Modelling

Cardboard engineering

Even though you are only using paper and card, when making the moving parts for pop-ups you might involve all the four main types of **motion**: linear, reciprocating, oscillating and rotary. You will also have to consider the main types of **forces**: tension, compression, torsion. Paper is weak in resisting all of these forces except one: which? With a strip of paper, try pulling each end (tension), pushing the ends toward each other (compression), and then twisting it (torsion).

Pop-ups have been made for centuries, so common techniques have been developed. The main methods used are shown below. Study the examples and then model some of your own ideas based on these methods. You will need paper, thin card, a rule, scissors, craft knives, cutting board, glue, adhesive tape and paper fasteners.

Manufacturing processes, page 65

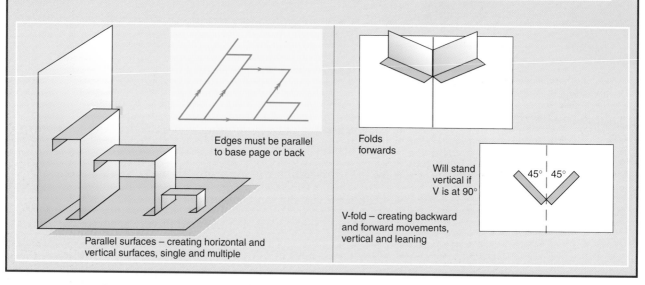

Edges must be parallel to base page or back

Parallel surfaces – creating horizontal and vertical surfaces, single and multiple

Folds forwards

Will stand vertical if V is at 90°

45° 45°

V-fold – creating backward and forward movements, vertical and leaning

Designing your pop-up product

Whether you are making a book with several pages or a single pop-up artefact, you need to make some decisions about the overall design.

- What graphics are needed?
- What pop-up mechanisms will bring them to life?
- What text is required?
- Where will the mechanisms, graphics and text be positioned?
- How do the graphics influence the pop-up and vice versa?

If you are designing a product with more than one page use a storyboard to plan the layout.

Pop-ups and flaps do not have to be in the middle of the page

The page can be a background picture

Place text where it will not be covered up accidentally

Some pages will need to be of double thickness to conceal mechanisms

D&T Routes Blue Book, page 18

Using accurate scale drawings

Modelling will show you how difficult it can be to make your idea work exactly how you want it to. To achieve the correct amount and direction of movement requires each part to be cut exactly to size, each fold line to be in exactly the right place and the positioning of each join to be precise.

Manufacturing industries aim for **right first time** for reasons of economy. A good way for you to achieve this is to use the techniques that manufacturers use. Construct full scale drawings of your design showing:

a) views of each pop-up, folded open, showing the positions of all the mechanisms (an **assembly drawing**).

b) views of the separate mechanisms (**sub-assemblies**).

c) each part of a mechanism separated out (**parts drawing**).

The best methods to use are **orthographic projection** and **isometric projection** making full use of **exploded views**.

Do not forget to allow for the thickness of the materials being used.

 D&T Challenges Red Book, pages 99–101

Once you have completed the scale drawings you can use the information to transfer the sizes to the materials.

Cutting out the parts

Your card or paper parts should be cut out using a sharp scalpel or craft knife on a cutting mat. Remember to use a safety rule or strong template,

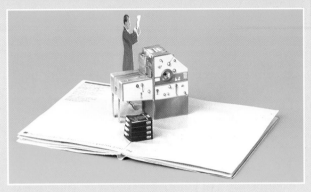

Kall-Kwik wanted something that would make their printing company 'stand out' from competitors. The pop-ups make the pictures arresting and fun.

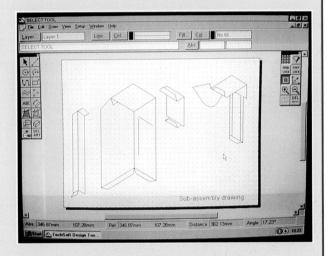

hold it beyond the knife and cut towards you, away from your fingers.

A more accurate method is to use a **plotter-cutter** as the output device for CAD drawings, provided that your sheet material is not too thick.

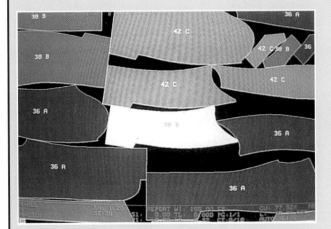
Pattern 'lays' minimising wastage.

Paper cut on a plotter-cutter.

Corporate identity

Your challenge

In today's fast changing business environment, a company must express its identity in everything it does
                              Wally Olins, Corporate Identity

Communicating the company's 'personality' or **corporate identity** has become extremely important for all forward thinking organisations. Many thousands of pounds are spent on creating the right image. This is then used to label all that the company does.

Your challenge is to create an identity for a company or organisation of your own choice. It might be a high street store, your own school or youth group or one of the country's leading companies.

Whatever it is, you must be imaginative in creating an **original** and **appropriate logo**, and clever in ensuring that it is suitable for use in a whole range of applications.

DfEE

Photograph courtesy of BT Corporate Picture Library

Why this activity is useful

This can be a real project giving evidence for interviews which might include: how well you can work with others, how creative you are and the quality you can produce.

You will have the opportunity to be very creative but must also be very practical, ensuring suitability for the identity's applications.

You will be able to create a unique identity of your own using a range of skills and equipment, experimenting with different techniques for reproducing the same 'graphic'.

You can begin to gain an understanding of how businesses and companies sell themselves and how important this is to them.

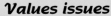

Values issues

◆ Trace the history of a company logo or image. Where did it start? How has it changed? Has it improved/become more effective?

◆ Companies spend great sums of money on improving their identity which can create a great deal of waste, disposing of the old style. Do you think this is defensible?

◆ Government departments spend a lot on their identities, especially when they are re-organised. Should the identity of bodies which have their power guaranteed by being 'official' cost the taxpayer money?

◆ How have advances in technology influenced organisations' need for a corporate identity?

To be successful

★ Investigate what the organisation you are designing for wishes to be associated with. How do they want to be viewed in the market-place?

★ Agree with the client a detailed specification including the full range of applications.

★ Present a folio of design development paying particular attention to the image's style, colour, proportions, and different applications.

★ Show your image applied to a professional standard on a range of appropriate products.

★ This will be a piece of your assessed coursework. You can increase your chances of exam success by being clear what the marking scheme expects from you.

How to get going

▶ Identify the organisation you will work for as soon as possible.

▶ Find out their expectations including words and pictures which they may require to be incorporated.

▶ Collect together a range of examples of corporate identities, analyse them (good /poor, famous/unknown, large/small scale) and discuss them as a group.

▶ Prepare your specification and criteria for a successful logo.

▶ Explore freely: colour, lettering styles, shape, form, layout.

▶ Try your image ideas on different products.

▶ Discuss and evaluate your work with your group or class to your original criteria/specification.

This has been done so often before, you will have to work hard to find something different. Be thorough with your research, adventurous with your ideas, rigorous with quality and have fun!

Corporate identity

CORPORATE IDENTITY

Investigating the organisation

Start off by thinking about the different types of organisation which you could design for. In groups make a list of some organisations which you are part of e.g. school, youth group, swimming club etc. How many of these have a corporate identity? Sketch their logo next to their name on your list.

Organisation	Type	Image
Design Council	National Government	Design Council
The W.13 Social Club	Voluntary/educational	THE W.13 SOCIAL CLUB FOR YOUNG PEOPLE
Eurostar	Commercial railway	eurostar
Loughborough University	Educational	Loughborough University
Wigmore Hall	Commercial concert hall	WIGMORE HALL

Now think of other organisations which you are familiar with: shops, manufacturers, other companies (maybe an organisation which people in your family work for), your local council etc. Scan through local and national newspapers, comics and magazines to identify these.

Approaching the organisation

It is important to identify the right person in the company to make the initial contact with. It might be the Managing Director or the Chief Executive Officer. It may be somebody based more locally, but it's not likely to be the person that serves you in the shop or answers the phone when you ring up.

Once you know who to contact, write a letter explaining who you are and what you want to do. It is important to be clear about what you will need to know and how you intend to do it.

D&T Routes Core Book,
Interviewing an expert, page 94

What to ask

You must first familiarise yourself with the business or organisation which you have chosen. Get some leaflets, company information or products. Look at their premises. Do they have a Web site? Look them up in Kelly's Directory. Find out as much as possible in advance then use the beginning of a visit to check and complete this information:

1 Structure

What is the organisation's main function/range of products?
What are the different parts of the organisation?
What does each part do?
How do the different bits relate to each other?

2 Symbolism

What is the ethos of the organisation?
What is their mission statement?
What are the main messages the organisation wants the public to receive?

3 Individualism

How does the organisation compare to its competitors?
What are the key features which make it different/better?
What would they want to add to this in the future?

Experimenting with text forms

The style, size and layout of lettering that you use can make a huge difference to an organisation's image. Lettering alone can even be the entire basis of a corporate identity. Be adventurous with trying out different ideas and think about how the letter shapes change the impression of the word. Use the examples to inspire you. Can you use a text-manipulation program on a computer to try different ideas, stretching and re-shaping initial forms? (See page 35).

Things to think about

- Different line thicknesses
- Serif or sans-serif
- Rounded or sharp edged letters
- The shape of whole words – stretched, wrapped, geometric or organic ones
- Shading
- Colour
- Clarity/legibility
- 3D forms it will be applied to

Experimenting with images

Hanson

(Hanson PLC)

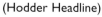

(Hodder Headline)

SHELL

Working for a fairer World

ChildLine

0800 1111

SHELL

HALIFAX

benefits

ba

agency

C H U R C H F I E L D S
VEHICLE RENTALS

The familiar Shell logo has evolved considerably in the last hundred years or so, and now needs no name in order to be recognised.

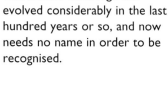

(Child Growth Foundation)

(Amnesty International)

National Power

Your company/organisation may already have a symbol or graphic. You may have to, or may want to retain this. However if you are starting from scratch:

- collect examples of existing logos/symbols
- use simple shapes to get you started
- experiment with letters and words
- try by joining/combining shapes
- investigate natural shapes or objects.

If you are developing/modifying a logo:

- investigate how long-standing companies have modified their logos
- concentrate on details
- think about 'modernising' or making the symbol more fashionable.

Case study

This page shows the application of a company's corporate identity to a number of different purposes. See how the logo relates to the company's product. Also look at how well the scheme works when used at different scales.

Thames Water Plc
Nugent House Vastern Road Reading
Berks RG1 8DB
Telephone 0118 959 1159

Direct Telephone 0118
Direct Fax 0118

Annual Report and Accounts 1997

Thames Water
CUSTOMER SERVICES

To get in touch about your bill

phone us on
0645 200888

and quote your account number
94159-65186

We are open 24 hours a day, 7 days a week.
Phoning us costs the same as a local call.

	Charge Value £	x	Rate pence/£	+	Standing Charge £	=	Totals £
Services for 1 APR 96 - 31 MAR 97							
Water supply charge	202		27.230		15.00		70.00
Sewerage charge	202		25.220		27.00		77.94
						Total £	147.94

PAYING THIS BILL
You can pay

RUNNING WATER
FOR YOU

Photostories

Your challenge

We live in a culture which is bursting with visual imagery created by broadcasting and the printed media. Many of these images are designed using **photography**, **video** and **computerised digital imaging** techniques. We see this abundance of imagery using the television, the Internet, CD-ROMs, videos, magazines, newspapers or books and many of these images are presented in sequences which tell a story.

The photostory in magazines and comics is one of the most popular and accessible forms of sequencing images, in which still images are used in conjunction with text to create a visually interesting story, usually aimed at young people.

Your challenge is to develop and design a photostory for a new magazine. You will have to consider the target audience, the magazine genre and the means of production.

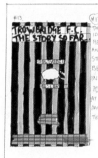

Why this activity is useful

You could learn how photographic or digital images are created and used in printed media.

You will learn about niche markets and target audiences within the magazine industry.

You will understand the use of scripting, storyboarding, visual and language conventions, layout design and photo shoots.

You could use photography and digital imaging software or simply drawing.

You will design and create your own photostory aimed at a target audience.

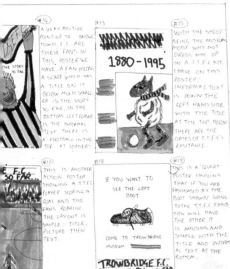

33

Royal College of Art
Postgraduate Art & Design

e are the only exclusively postgraduate university c
t and design in the world, with the authority to conf
ster's and Doctoral degrees: the most concentrated
mmunity of young artists and designers to be found
where...

Values issues

◆ What types of magazines primarily carry photostories and why?
◆ How do photostories reflect the values and the preoccupations of their target audience?
◆ Some people feel that the values explored by photostories are too concerned with romance and personal problems. Design a questionnaire that investigates the appeal of photostories and their values – present the results as a chart.
◆ What other cultural values/issues could be explored using the medium of the photostory?

To be successful

★ You will need to:
– research several different magazine photostories and analyse the use of images, text/language, layout, design and visual conventions
– find out more about photography and digital imagery in terms of equipment, lighting, framing, composition and composing an image
– write an appropriate story script for your intended target audience
– acquire production skills in photography and/or digital imaging or drawing to achieve a high quality product.
★ Could you produce a multi-media photostory and put it on the Internet?
★ This will be a piece of your assessed coursework. You will increase your chances of exam success by being clear what the marking scheme expects from you.

How to get going

◗ Produce a storyboard, designing the image sequences you intend to use.
◗ Think about appropriate dialogue and visual layout.
◗ From the storyboard, produce a mock-up of your intended layout and design.
◗ Plan a production schedule for your photostory. Consider such problems as:
– equipment
– personnel
– locations/transport
– cost
– time allocations
– costumes/continuity
– technical support
– design and production of final product.

Packaging

We are surrounded with packaging – many people come into contact with as many as 250 pieces a day. Much of it we take for granted, yet it all provides some service, getting products to us fresh, clean and undamaged. The packaging can play many roles: the key ones are to advertise the product and attract our attention, to inform us about the contents, to protect both us and the product and to contain the product in the most appropriate way.

Your challenge is to select a product and create a new look for it by designing the packaging and the graphics that go on it. You may wish to change how the pack functions and the shape of the package, as well as the graphic images on it.

Why this activity is useful

You will realise the importance of the appearance and function of packaging.

You will learn that graphics and packaging design can affect how people react to products, providing information, attracting new customers, protecting the product and making it easier to store and transport.

You will gain insights into a major industry that employs many people.

You will have the opportunity to look at ways of becoming a more responsible designer, thinking about economy in design, waste of materials and reducing pollution.

Values issues

◆ During the political changes in Russia during the early 1990s up to 50% of fresh food was wasted due to poor packaging for transportation, so the food arrived at its destination unsuitable for consumption. What would be the minimum packaging needed to prevent such terrible waste of money and precious resources?

◆ Different products may allow for different improvements to be made. Here are some to consider.
  – Can environmental impact be reduced by responsible designing?
  – How can waste be reduced in manufacturing packages?
  – How can the packaging be more economical?
  – Can the materials be lessened to reduce transport costs and use less natural resources?
  – Where can we get information to make choices about recycled or recyclable materials?

To be successful

★ Clearly identify the customer of your product (the target audience) and the style to suit them.

★ Draw up a specification for your packaging covering at least the key areas: informing, containing, attracting and protecting.

★ Make a mood board based on your chosen style to help you choose colours and graphic effects.

★ Choose appropriate materials and techniques to make your package and apply the graphics.

★ Find out about making a package in large quantities and how this would affect your costs and your design plans.

★ This will be a piece of assessed coursework. You can increase your chances of success by being clear what the marking scheme expects from you.

How to get going

◗ Look carefully at existing packaging across competing products. Evaluate them to help your designing.

◗ Investigate the materials and processes that are available.

◗ Look in a wide variety of places (books, magazines, TV, shops etc.) for inspiration and source materials for your mood board.

◗ Try out your ideas by making prototypes.

◗ Test your graphic ideas on other people to see if their responses are as you had planned.

◗ Use your test results to improve your designs.

Construction play

Card is one of the most common materials. We are surrounded with card packaging, most of which is eventually thrown away. Think for a moment about how you used this readily available material as a child: boxes to play in; boxes to cut up and build with; a material to cut up and make masks with, or glue together to create models. Did you ever put aside the toy and play with the box it came in?

Your challenge is to investigate how children of various ages play with card packaging, the games they play or the models they make. You should then develop **prototypes** and **nets** which could be printed on the surface of packaging to stimulate children to play.

Why this activity is useful

You will develop the sophistication and the scope of your modelling skills.

Genuine research observations need to be made – in a real situation.

You will work within very tight restrictions on material size, depending on your chosen carton, and will learn about appropriate printing methods. By developing ideas for young children you will come to understand how to channel their creativity, through using waste materials.

You will be raising your awareness of environmental issues.

You will undertake on-going testing and evaluate your product throughout this challenge.

Values issues

- Many people feel that we waste materials in this country. Some governments impose additional taxes on products which have excessive packaging or packaging which is non-returnable. Discuss these issues within your design folio.

- Many stores which sell pack-flat furniture in plain cardboard cartons also sell useful household products made from similar cardboard. Is there scope for developing the idea of re-using packaging?

- There are some important books on the issues described above e.g. Victor Papanek: *Design for the Real World* & E F Schumacher: *Small is Beautiful*. Find out if these writers are available in your library and read their ideas.

Card model of a shop interior.

To be successful

- ★ Research into a specific aspect of children's play and record your findings. Make full use of photography, observational drawing, video etc. as well as a written or spoken report.

- ★ Focus on a specific carton which offers potential for play and develop a range of ideas which could lead to directions for use printed onto the carton's surface.

- ★ Make prototypes which demonstrate what the printed net (or development) would look like on the carton. And how it will look when made up in its 3D form.

- ★ Evaluate your prototype by testing with children of the appropriate age group.

- ★ This will be a piece of your assessed coursework. You can increase your chances of success by being clear what the marking scheme expects from you.

Cardboard model of a shop front.

How to get going

- Arrange to observe children playing with cardboard boxes, perhaps in a local nursery. Alternatively, you might work as a whole class to collect a range of cartons, paints, scissors etc. and invite a group of young children into your school. You might consider doing a similar activity with older children to compare the differences.

- Talk to adults about their observations and record their ideas.

- You will need to develop your ideas mainly through modelling. Additional research may be necessary, especially if your ideas are to be made up to into accurate models.

Getting the picture

Your challenge

'Richest Person in the World is Worth $18 BILLION', or was that $18 million? If he has a 3.5% rise what would he be worth then? How much better off would you be with 3.5% more? How much better off is the richest person than you?

Almost every day on the television news, graphics are used to help people make sense of numbers and to see the relationships between them. There's quite a difference between 18 billion and 18 million – how can we make this clear? How do graphic symbols liven-up obscure numbers to catch people's interest and aid understanding?

Your challenge is to take some real numbers – from a newspaper or other public source – and present them to other people in a way that is lively and clear.

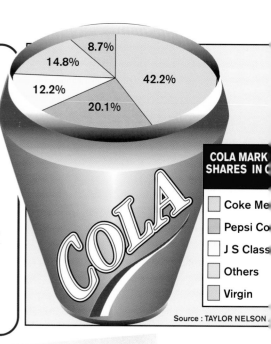

COLA MARK... SHARES IN C...

- Coke Me...
- Pepsi Co...
- J S Class...
- Others
- Virgin

8.7%
14.8%
12.2%
42.2%
20.1%

Source : TAYLOR NELSON

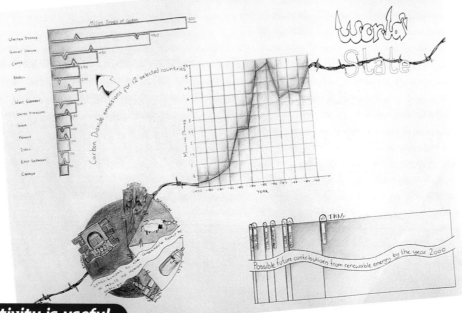

Why this activity is useful

People learn about numbers in various different ways and many people learn better when using information for a real purpose. This work could help you develop mathematical concepts that are vital to many areas of technology.

It could also give you a chance to do something really worthwhile for your school, a club or other organisation. This could be impressive on your record of achievement or CV.

Using visual presentation purposefully like this will improve your understanding of the power of graphics – to make the truth clear, or to distort it.

Values issues

◆ *There are lies, damn lies and statistics* is often said. Statistical information always needs to be interpreted and this always involves some choices about the most important messages they convey.

◆ Get some company annual reports (possibly from your Business Studies department) and see what aspects of their statistics are being emphasised and which are played-down. (This is called 'putting a spin on them'.)

◆ Find some comments from a politician and see if you can trace the influence of a 'spin doctor' on their presentation.

◆ Try representing the same statistics in two different ways, each to draw people to opposite conclusions.

To be successful

★ To do this assignment well you will have to understand the figures you are presenting very well. Analyse them thoroughly and test your understanding on others before going ahead.

★ Explore a wide range of ideas for the graphic presentation of your data, it should be dynamic, eye-catching, humorous perhaps and, above all, effective in communication.

★ The quality of presentation should be as good as you would expect on television. Use materials and methods that give a really professional finish.

★ This will be a piece of your assessed coursework. You can increase your chances of exam success by being clear about what the marking scheme expects from you.

How to get going

▶ Your school will use numbers in many ways: attendance rates, examination statistics, age profiles, assessments of progress etc., which you might be able to present for Governors' or parents' meetings.

▶ Do you have a hobby or other interest that can have numerical information about it displayed graphically?

▶ Use maths books to find out what types of graph you might use: pictograms, histograms, pie charts. Think about which would best show the relationship between the numbers you are portraying.

▶ See if you can use a graphing calculator to help you, and find out what computer programs are available which can generate the initial graphs for you.

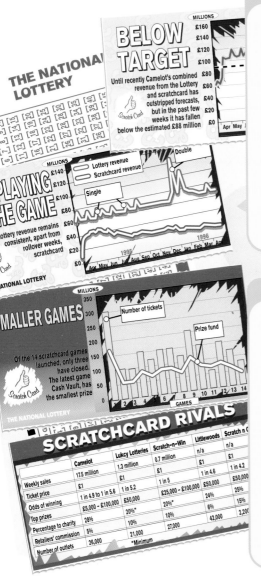

Three-dimensional T-shirts

Your challenge

Sometimes a product is no more than a vehicle for its graphics. For example some textile products, such as T-shirts, may be worn mainly for their graphic images rather than as garments in their own right. They become graphic products that you can wear.

Comfort may be important but wearing a T-shirt for its appearance will mean that shape, colour and look are just as important.

Should T-shirt graphics only be 2D printed or could you develop ideas into 3D forms to be worn in the same way as words and slogans?

Your challenge is to extend T-shirt graphics into a 3D form. Remember it will be a worn garment, so think about how the user will look.

Why this activity is useful

Designing and making these products will broaden your experience into textiles and other materials.

You can experiment with very unusual ideas and challenge accepted views.

You will increase your understanding of shape and form and apply graphic treatments to a wider range of surfaces.

You will have to balance fun with comfort, wearability and aesthetics.

You will have the opportunity to explore a wide range of initial ideas and to be very creative, developing new and unusual ideas for T-shirts.

Values issues

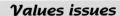

◆ What new kinds of graphic images would people like to wear if they could?
◆ Would some images be wrong because they might offend others?
◆ Should people be allowed to wear any images or slogans, or should the law fix limits, as it does in some countries?
◆ Where will this product be worn? E.g. is it for a special occasion, party, or general use?

To be successful

You will be changing the accepted design of T-shirts so you also need to think about manufacturability, or how difficult your design would be to make.

★ Clarify precisely what your design intentions are.
★ Produce and meet a specification.
★ Model your ideas carefully before deciding to work on a real T-shirt.
★ Think carefully about materials and practical considerations such as laundering.
★ Show how your design would be suitable for volume production.
★ This will be a piece of your assessed coursework. You can increase your chances of success by being clear what the marking scheme expects from you.

How to get going

★ Which places on the T-shirt would allow 3D objects to grow from them? Model a T-shirt, full size, using thin detail paper attached to a stiff card backing. It will help to bring a real T-shirt into school so that you can examine it more closely and make your model as realistic as possible.
★ Consider adapting skills such as air-brushing, shading, shadow and colouring to 3D surfaces by carrying out tests and working carefully on a life-size model.
★ When you have sketched and put forward several ideas you can develop them further, in 3D, on your model.
★ You can use and adapt many kinds of throw-away objects to build up the 3D form needed on the T-shirt model.
★ Think about ways of using workshop processes, such as vacuum-forming and fabrication, to generate the forms you need.
★ Check your ergonomics: think about how the design will feel when it is worn and whether it will be washable.
★ You may decide that your model goes far enough or you could take it further into a real T-shirt prototype later.

Explore many different ideas – have fun – but avoid ideas that might give offence to others.

DESIGNING

Graphic products

What does **graphic** mean? Originally this word referred to written descriptions, however today it can be used in relation to most kinds of **visual communication**. A dictionary will tell you that graphic information can be drawn, vividly described, written or visually presented. How does this help you to identify the graphic product that you might design and manufacture in design and technology? You need to be clear about products that are graphic in nature and those that are not. Also, your examination board may have regulations that exclude some types of project work from being assessed as graphic products, so you need to be sure that your teacher makes their rules clear.

How graphic products are useful or important to us

Graphic products are very important to us in our everyday lives. From our earliest days in childhood we are exposed to, and influenced by, them. They may do one or more of these things:

◆ make information more accessible to us e.g. road maps, telephone directories, bar charts
◆ impose information on us by influencing our thinking (possibly subconsciously) e.g. advertising to persuade us to buy a particular product
◆ help us to communicate our feelings and identity to others e.g. by wearing a certain T-shirt
◆ warn us of potential dangers e.g. safety signs, road signs
◆ appeal to our emotions e.g. anti-vivisection posters
◆ help us to lead a more responsible life by increasing our awareness e.g. charity posters.

Graphic forms of communication are also vital to business and industry and provide a convenient way for companies to give out information that needs to be known.

Corporate identities may be seen in many forms, including signs, symbols and brand marking on many kinds of products. When graphics are used to persuade, or inform the purchasing decisions that people make, they are known as **promotional graphics**.

Sometimes familiar symbols and signs are used to persuade us to make purchasing decisions.

Packaging also provides opportunities to communicate, persuade, drop hints and make suggestions that can influence purchasing decisions. The surfaces of packages are so convenient for this that they have developed into a field of graphics in their own right.

> ### Focused task: Graphic identities
>
> Find an example of each of the following:
>
> ■ corporate identity
> ■ promotional graphics
> ■ an example of packaging that uses either of the above.
>
> Write a brief explanation of each of these graphic products to explain what you think the business or company intended to communicate.

Graphics as modelling

It is normal to 'think out loud' when designing by using graphic techniques, such as sketching or drawing. We often need to explore our early design ideas or present finished ones in the form of diagrams, engineering drawings or data charts. We can use graphics as a designing tool to help with every aspect of design and technology work, but these drawings are not themselves graphic products because they are just part of the process of designing a product.

Graphics as products in their own right

When designing and making products in D&T we are trying to satisfy a need through developing a manufactured product of some kind. If it is a graphic product its primary purpose will be to **communicate messages**. It can also be used to suggest secondary meanings associated with the main messages. These **associated meanings** can help graphic products to communicate more powerfully than the written or spoken word.

Graphic products as a D&T focus area

Some graphic products have a very clear graphic purpose.

Products from other D&T focus areas may also carry graphic messages. But how important are these messages to the primary function of the product?

 D&T Routes Core Book, Primary and secondary functions, page 66

Stop and think

When is a product a graphic product?

A graphic product can be concerned solely with communication or may have other purposes e.g. packaging, to protect the goods it contains.

Is it right to put slogans and other persuasive messages on products that could exist well without them?

This graphic product consists of photographs and text.

Graphic products

Focused task: *Products carrying graphics*

1 List some examples of products that carry powerful messages, in the form of graphics.

2 Look at each object/group of objects in the photographs here and add five more of your own. Place them on a scale of one to five, judging the importance of graphic communication to the object.

These chocolate wrappers have a graphic function, but this is not their primary function.

Identifying a need for a graphic product

In addition to the messages which have to be communicated, the **function** of the product and the **environment** in which it is to be used must also be considered.

It is likely that the designer will have other considerations such as ergonomics, resistance to degradation, cost and appropriate choice of materials, to name just a few.

To help you focus on graphic products in D&T use these questions:

◆ What does my graphic product do and what makes it graphic?
◆ What messages is it communicating?
◆ Is it a graphic product or graphics on a product?

This acrylic shop sign is a graphic product but it also had to be formed in resistant materials to survive exposure to the weather.

◆ Does my graphic product develop into another form of product at some point? If so, how far must I develop it before its success can be judged?

DESIGNING

30

Generating ideas

Initial images

Where do ideas for graphic products come from? The process of designing a graphic product is similar to designing other kinds of D&T products. However, it is likely that your graphic product will need to carry messages or special meanings to work in the way you intend. This will rely on the visual images you use.

Inspiration for these images can come from many sources, so you can use various techniques to get your ideas flowing. Try the ones from page 53 of the *D&T Routes Core Book*. Also, be clear about the purposes of your product.

What do you need to communicate?

What does your product need to say? Is it:

◆ what your client wants?
◆ a message or meaning which goes onto a product at a later stage?
◆ a personal statement of your own?

Will the information be 'read' in a particular order?

Layout, page 45

Target audiences

If your product carries messages you must consider carefully who the messages are going to – your **target audience**. You will need to think carefully about how they would respond.

Is your target audience:

◆ a particular age group?
◆ a work or occupation group?
◆ people who have a common interest of some kind? What is it?

Thinking about these questions may help you to word your text appropriately and source the right images that will meet your particular need.

◆ What kinds of graphic image will best suit your need?
◆ What styles will attract your 'audience'?
◆ Where can you look for ideas and inspiration?

Focused task: Target audiences

1 Write a 'customer profile' which describes the target audience for six magazines that you know or can find out about. Choose magazines with different target audiences. For example:

Vogue	Spectator	GQ
Car	Cosmopolitan	Mad
Mountain Biking	Bike	New Statesman
Bliss	Sugar	Punch
Viz		

2 Attach an image to each title which you feel sums up its target audience. Be prepared to be quite abstract with this.

Beware – with some products the buyer might not be the user. Take children's toys for instance – who buys them and who uses them? Does this make a difference:

■ to the marketing?
■ to the packaging?
■ to the product?

tipper truck

Developing ideas

One important way in which your graphic product will be judged is by how well it **communicates** what you or your client intend. Does it get the message across? Special graphic techniques may be needed to achieve this and you will need to make decisions at every stage as your design develops. You will probably have to change your mind from time to time as well.

Keep a record as these developments take place, remembering to use an appropriate style of presentation to communicate, both for yourself and others.

Planning, choosing and using graphic techniques all play an important part in designing and making a successful graphic product.

Your ideas and proposals might be sketched, drawn or explained in various ways. Various techniques commonly used by graphic designers may help you.

Initial product ideas – starting loose and tightening-up

Collect together all your images and information related to the subject. Look at how other designers have handled similar topics. In the early stages concentrate on transferring many different thoughts and ideas rapidly onto paper, avoiding unnecessary detail that might restrict your flow of ideas at this stage. You might sketch with a medium or soft pencil (between HB and 4B), working in a relaxed way. Or you could work directly in colour with crayons, felt tips or ballpoint to move ideas quickly

forward. Concentrate on generating different ideas rather than detailing or changing each one. You can return to each later.

Be prepared to create more accurate sketches and work out details and measurements once you have a range of ideas. Working with slightly harder pencils at this stage (between HB and 2H) will give a crisp line and greater accuracy. You might also now use drawing aids, such as set squares, a compass and templates.

Client presentation

If you are working for a client, you will need to gain approval for your design. Professional designers on a large project may have two or three stages at which they make a presentation to their clients. You should at least expect to make a presentation once your design is nearly complete and before committing yourself to manufacturing. Your client might not be an expert, so choosing an appropriate way to present to them is important. For example, a **technical drawing** might show accuracy but might also confuse an inexperienced person. A clear, **rendered perspective drawing**, showing textures and finish, might give a better idea for your client to comment on.

Choosing the best combination of methods and techniques may rely on a variety of factors including: the budget, materials available, the client's expectations or demands, and the presentation arrangements.

Work as loosely as you can to free-up your ideas.

Communicating through written words has been crucial to human progress. Just think how much information is carried through text, including books, newspapers, CD-ROMs and the Internet. However, pictures preceded writing and they still can convey more information, more efficiently. Think hard about what you should communicate through words and what through visuals. Too many words can be a problem but for short messages, like product labels and headlines, words can have tremendous impact.

Our alphabet evolved from the written letter forms of the Phoenicians (about 1600BC). These were adapted by the ancient Greeks (1000BC) and then adapted by the Romans. The Roman alphabet forms the basis of many of our modern alphabets.

Modern Western letter forms can be traced back 2000 years to ancient Rome.

Most of the vocabulary of text design derives from printing methods which used solid metal letters, so letters are usually referred to as **type** and anything to do with the arrangement of lettering is called **typography**. It is easy to underestimate the importance of typography – there is much more to it than just being neat.

The typography in each of these products was carefully designed for its intended purpose.

Different kinds of type

Differences in lettering include **size**, **weight** (the thickness of the letter strokes) and **design** – each different design is called a **typeface**. Printers stored separate typefaces in boxes called founts (or **fonts**) and this term is still used: you will meet it when using a word-processor. Well designed graphic products use appropriate typography where each of these can make an important difference:

Size

Type is measured in special units called **points** and **picas** although millimetres can be used as well. There are approximately 6 picas in an inch and there are 12 points in 1 pica so there are approximately 72 points in 25 mm.

Typeface

In the early printing industry, a specially shaped block of type, called a **typeface**, was used to impress the printing ink onto the paper. The handmade and ink coated 'face of the type' gave the letters their appearance. There are many different typeface (or font) designs and each has its own name. There are two main groups of typefaces, serif and sans-serif as shown on the next page.

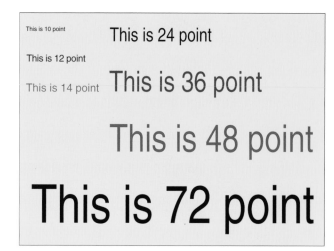

Different point sizes

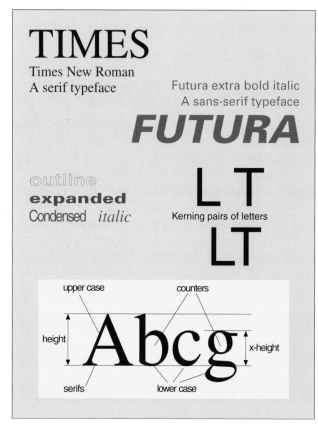

Variations in type

Using different type styles for emphasis

Typefaces often belong to a type family which share the same basic design but which can vary in weight or in stress e.g. italic or roman (upright). Members of a type family can be used to emphasise different kinds of information e.g. bold for headlines, regular for text, and italic for captions.

Spacing

Space added between lines of type is referred to as **leading**, space between words as **word spacing** and space between individual characters as letter spacing (or **kerning**).

Lettering techniques

Calligraphy

Lettering that is produced by hand, using brushes or nibbed pens, is known as calligraphy. This is still a popular craft, especially in Japan.

Visualising type by hand

Drafting type by hand, working as accurately as you can, is the simplest way of visualising possible ideas or producing prototypes. It is especially useful for major headlines and product names. Neat and accurate work is essential to get the feel of a particular typeface or style. Letters can be traced over examples from type books or photocopied sheets of the right size. With practice you can achieve a good result as well as carry out experiments of your own.

DESIGNING

Examples of students' lettering work

Dry transfer

Pre-formed, self-adhesive letters can be transferred from special sheets onto the piece of work. This form of lettering gives a very high quality result but is also very expensive. Great care is needed to get word and letter spacing correct. Most students prefer the flexibility of a word-processor.

Dry transfer lettering

Lettering stencils

Drawing inside a pre-formed plastic shape, or stencil, helps control the letter shape but means that extra pieces, needed to hold the stencil together, intrude. The result is rather utilitarian – packing cases often have stencil type lettering.

Using computers for lettering

Good word-processors allow some control over lettering but desktop publishing programs let the designer see and modify more aspects of typographic designs on screen before being printed out. Typefaces can be stretched, compressed and distorted in many ways, including wrapping around a 3D object. Different colours and shades can also be applied.

The computer has simplified the printing of words and given considerable flexibility to the designer over shapes and styles.

Stop and think

What reasons are there for the development of your typographic design? How do they improve your product? In particular, consider:

- are the words easy to read?
- does your lettering have an individual personality?
- does the style of the lettering suit the subject?
- would a computer program make it easier to produce alternative designs?
- have you gone 'over the top'?

Remember the KISS principle: 'Keep it Simple, Stupid'.

Lettering

DESIGNING

Focused task: Lettering styles

1 Select two different existing products' names, one food and one sport or fashion. Dividing your paper into four, draw (at least part of) the two names to the same size, using guidelines and hand-lettering, in the top two quarters of the page. Prepare the same size guidelines in the bottom two sections and repeat the words but swap the typefaces exactly. Pay close attention to all the characteristics especially the styles i.e. italic or upper or lower case.

   Observe the effect: does it change the impression given by the lettering of each product? If so, explain why you think this has happened with brief notes under each example.

2 Choose a simple typeface: serif or sans-serif. Hand-letter a word, linked with your project work, at least 20 mm high. Then produce it again, underneath the original but in a different style, remembering to keep all the key characteristics of the typeface. Consider changing such things as outline, italic and shadows.

These drawings were created by South African bush tribes, possibly to meet certain spiritual needs.

Sketching and drawing

For thousands of years sketching and drawing have been among the most commonly used communication methods.

Our ability to create visual images, including sketching and drawing, forms the basis for designing most products.

Stop and think

The two pictures on this page show some very different graphics.

- What differences do you see in these two examples of drawing?
- Do you think they both serve the same kind of purpose?
- Is one better than the other?

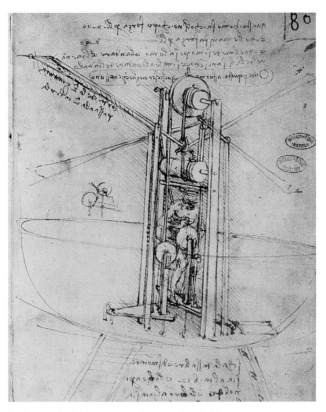

In the early 16th century Leonardo da Vinci was able to develop and communicate ideas for this flying machine through sketching and drawing.

Sketching and drawing

Sketching techniques

Sketching is the most versatile and important aid to communicating when designing. It should be informal but always accurate, usually fairly quick and lacking detail. You can sketch from observation or your imagination, recall from memory, crate, construct, correct and line-in to produce a good quality drawing very quickly.

 D&T Routes Core Book, Modelling, page 96

Using simple tools when sketching will allow you to concentrate on the drawing. A sharp B or HB pencil used lightly, will allow mistakes to be easily put right before lining in.

With practice, a fine-line pen can also be used to achieve a range of line weights for construction, modification and lining in. Skilfully handled, your early construction grids will be hardly noticeable. But remember that using ink makes correction difficult in the later stages of a drawing, so care is needed here.

Sketching allows you to generate, model and develop your ideas long before your product becomes a real object. This provides many time and cost-saving benefits.

If you line-in with a sharp pencil, then rub out leaving a feint impression, you can draw the product back in more smoothly without the mistakes and construction lines.

Drawing soft corners.

Planning your sketch using crates

You can improve your sketching by the use of simple **crates**, or 3D construction lines which identify the space an object will occupy.

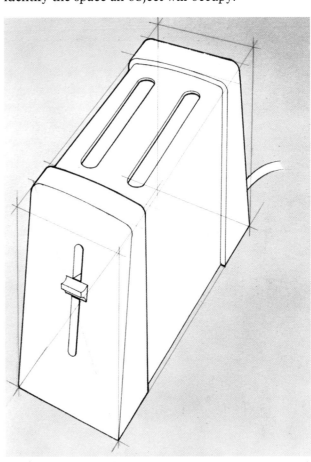

A crate can help you to plan and organise your sketch.

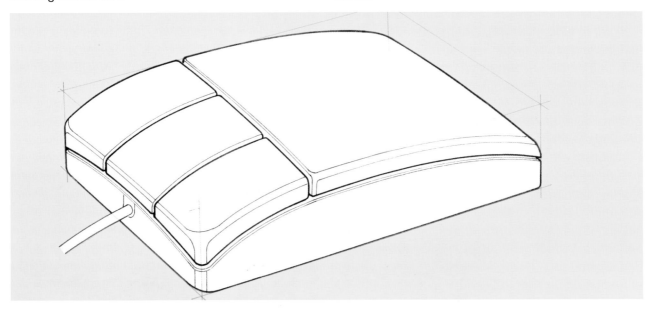

Formal drawing

You will eventually need to record and communicate features of your design more exactly than is possible through unaided sketching. More exact, or formal, drawing techniques include forms of **pictorial drawing**, **exploded drawings** and **orthographic projections**. Each of these methods might be appropriate to different stages of your designing or for different purposes. Choose the method that best suits what you intend to communicate, including size, shape, material, texture, function, construction and manufacturing requirements.

Pictorial drawing: Isometric

Making an **isometric** view involves turning all horizontal lines at 30° (usually) to the horizontal. You will therefore require a 30° set square or a pre-drawn grid for your construction.

This method of drawing turns a square into a rhombus and a circle into an ellipse.

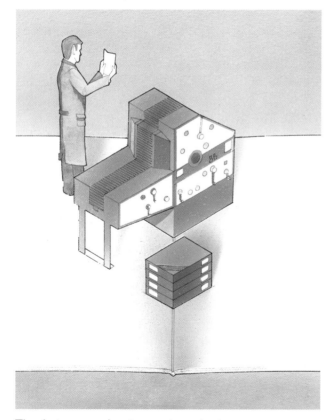

The designer used an isometric projection to make this pop-up page clear (see also page 11).

 Isometric Projection, D&T Challenges Red Book, page 101

Exploded drawing

'Pulled apart', or **exploded** drawings, can be used to more clearly show information about construction and internal detail. They can be exploded isometrics, orthographics (see page 40) or any other form of drawing.

When making an exploded drawing you must plan carefully, thinking about the direction, or axis, along which the individual parts should be 'exploded'.

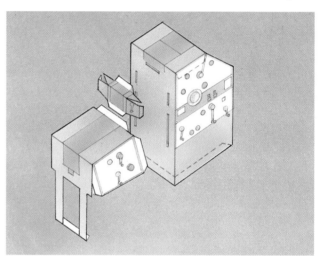

Important information about this design was shown using exploded isometric drawing.

Perspective drawing

A **perspective** drawing represents an object as you really see it – representing the illusion of things appearing smaller the further they are from you. A final design, drawn in perspective, can be made to look very realistic and give important information such as form, detail, texture and materials so can be very important for a client presentation.

Perspective drawings can be constructed, using special measured drawing procedures, or estimated using guesswork and judgement to decide proportions. Measured perspective is very difficult so you should concentrate on developing your 'eye' for good proportions and correct angles.

DESIGNING

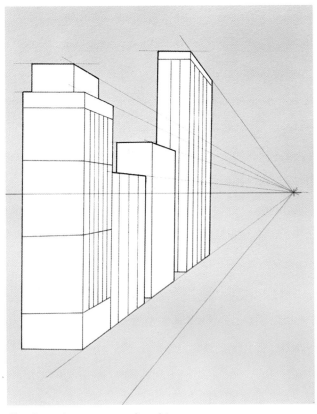

Single-point perspective. Lines converge to a single vanishing point. If parallel to the ground they will meet on the horizon.

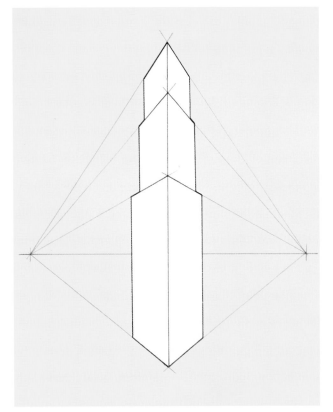

Two-point perspective. More realism is gained by the use of two vanishing points. All vertical lines remain vertical whilst other lines converge to the vanishing points.

There are three types of perspective drawing: one-point, two-point and three-point. All parallel lines on the object are deliberately drawn so that the distance between them grows smaller (**converges**) eventually disappearing at one or more **vanishing points**. To determine the vanishing points you will first need to draw a horizon, or imaginary line, which would be level with the eyes of the viewer. The vanishing points for horizontal lines are located on the horizon when making a perspective drawing.

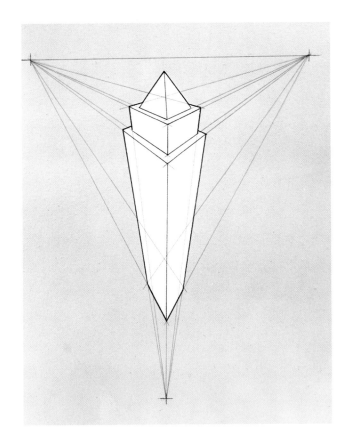

Three-point perspective. A third vanishing point is added above or below the object depending on where the viewer is positioned.

Formal drawing

Working drawings in orthographic projection

In orthographic projection, each part of a product is drawn several times, viewed from different positions. A similar technique is used to show all the parts together in a **general arrangement** (GA) drawing. Correct orthographic projection of these views, where each single view is positioned in a standard relationship to each other, allows the manufacturer to read precise detail from the drawing. A top view (plan), front view and end view, shown together, are usually expected of the designer by the manufacturer.

Orthographic projection is controlled by international standards so that a drawing can be reliably read in any part of the world. There are two ways of arranging the views in orthographic projection, called first angle and third angle. You should take care to be clear which you are using when making or reading a drawing.

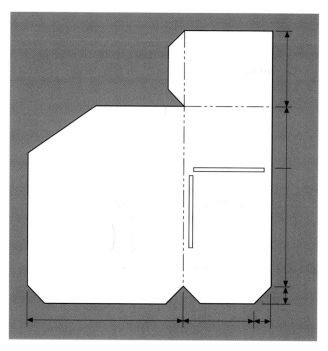

Orthographic projection used to show details clearly.

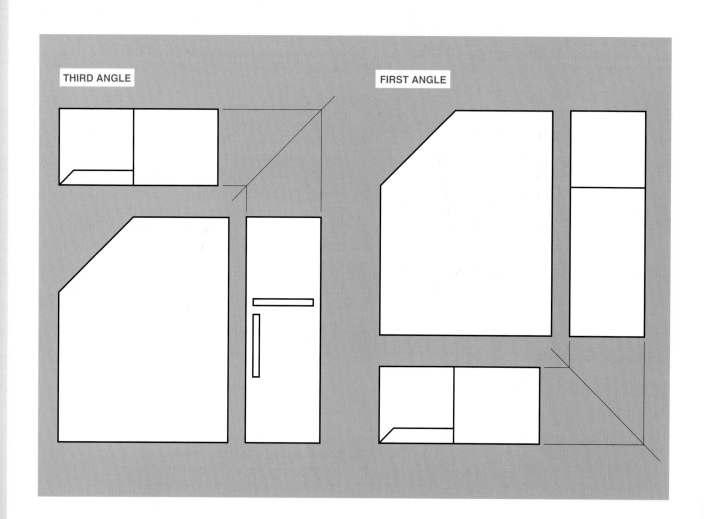

THIRD ANGLE

FIRST ANGLE

Working drawings may also need an extra view, such as a section of part of the object. This will show the object cut through so that the internal details can be easily seen.

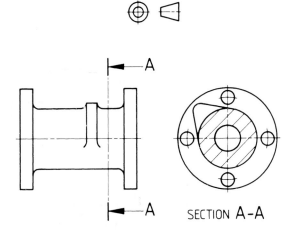

SECTION A-A

Scale

Drawing to International Standards (ISO) or British Standards (BS) will mean using a scale, adding dimensions to show how big the object and its component parts are, using the correct line types and adding the appropriate symbol for first or third angle. To do these things accurately you will need to be familiar with information from a standards manual, BS308 or PD7308 (Engineering Drawing Practice for Schools and Colleges).

Modelling to a **true scale**, that is exactly full size dimensions (sometimes including weight), gives a design accuracy and realism allowing us to appreciate its qualities better. Often drawings have to be **scaled down** (smaller than full size, e.g. 1:5) to fit onto your paper.

Occasionally drawings are **scaled up** (drawn larger than full size, e.g. 5:1) to show details clearly. An example of this is the design of integrated circuits (ICs) or computer 'chips'.

Drawing on a computer is different because the program will usually store the information with all the proportions and relationships as for full size. But the size of screen image will depend on the size of the monitor and images can be sent to print at a variety of sizes including full size and percentages of full size (either larger or smaller). For CAD/CAM, information is normally stored as full size and output will automatically follow this.

Using scaling standards

Scales for drawing are laid down by British Standards, including BS308 (or PD7308) and published so that designers and manufacturers can apply them correctly. Check your library for a copy when you need them. You might notice that fractional scales such as one quarter or one eighth are not used in the metric system. One fifth (or 1:5) is though – why is this?

> ### Focused task: *Drawing techniques*
>
> Find some products of different shapes and sizes. For each, sketch a crate that is in proportion with the object. For example:
>
> - draw a freehand perspective sketch of your household toaster
> - draw a freehand isometric sketch of a food processor
> - make an orthographic drawing of a simple household object, such as a stapler, using accurate measurements
> - working from memory, produce a freehand exploded drawing of a personal hi-fi, showing the open lid and cassette
> - produce a working drawing of a simple item with all the information needed for manufacture.

Geometrical drawing

Geometrical drawing deals with lines and spaces through mathematical construction rather than calculation. Early geometry was used to establish proportions and understand spatial relationships.

Geometric constructions can be very useful when special shapes have to be drawn very accurately or are too difficult to draw without the aid of instruments.

Line division can also be very useful when creating or using a scale to draw objects that would be too big or too small if drawn their normal (full) size.

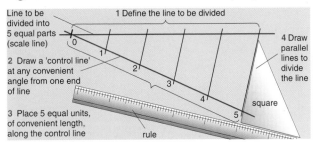

A scale can be created using line division.

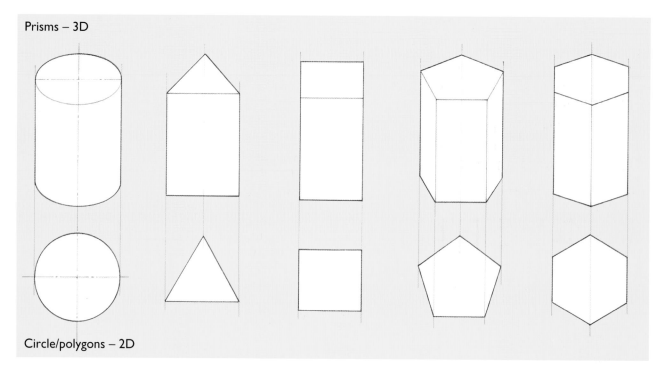

Prisms – 3D

Circle/polygons – 2D

Polygons are two-dimensional **plane** shapes, but can be made three-dimensional by adding height or thickness. When this is done the resulting shape is known as a **prism**.

Cylindrical forms are based on circles and are used frequently in presentation drawings.

The circle in a curved product may appear similar to an ellipse when drawn in isometric. Knowledge of geometry may help to construct it but designers use templates to save time.

Geometry or templates may be used to draw the ellipses in cylindrical forms.

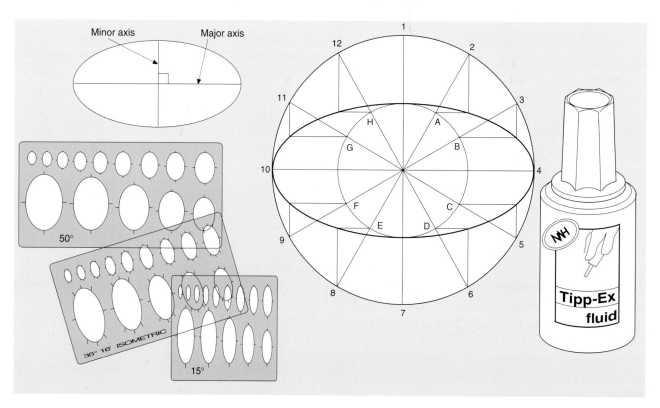

DESIGNING

Geometry on a computer

Sometimes geometry is used to test or check information at the design stage. Increasingly the computer is used rather than hand methods, due to its greater accuracy.

You might be able to use a computer to test your product in school. Or perhaps you will need a computer to divide up a space very accurately.

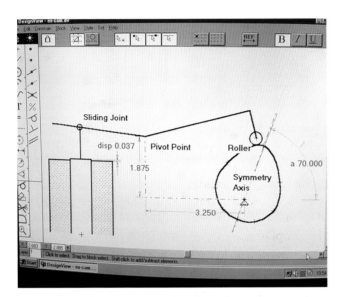

This Design View program is being used to test the design of a cam and follower for a control product being designed in school. The path of this mechanism is plotted on screen and its performance can be checked against the movement that is required.

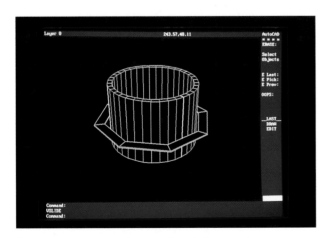

A computer was used to work out the spacing for these brackets on a seating project at George Ward School.

Colour in graphics

The colour of something can affect our feelings about it, our moods and can catch our attention. When products appear in unusual colours we are sometimes taken by surprise or find them difficult to accept.

People in other lands, or from different cultures, may feel quite differently to you about colours. In China brides wear red and funeral dress is white.

We get many of our ideas, including colour schemes and patterns, from nature. The yellow and black stripes of a wasp warn its enemies to beware.

Stop and think

- What other colour associations does nature give us?
- How important is it to understand cultural differences? Might this be important to your product's design?
- Should we accept the colours commonly used for products or can they be challenged?
- How might your choice of colour be influenced if you are designing a product for the international market?

Think carefully about your choice of colour when designing and making products. In particular:

- how will the user react to your colour scheme?
- why might certain colours have this affect rather than others?
- is there a recognised standard for your product? E.g. red for stop or green for go? If so, do you need to follow it?

DESIGNING

Create your own chart, in the form of a **colour wheel**, to help analyse and choose colours for products.

Explain the following, using annotations, on your own colour wheel:

- primary colours are three colours that cannot be made by mixing other colours
- secondary colours are made by mixing any two of the primary colours
- complementary colours are the pairs of colours opposite each other in the colour wheel and look very bright when positioned together.

Remember to experiment with different colours and techniques. Ask your teacher what colour media you have in your school. You might find some or all of the following: poster, acrylic, water colours, paper/board in matt and gloss varieties, markers and crayons.

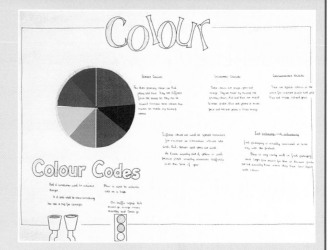

A student analysis of colour relationships for graphic products.

Using the computer to experiment with colour

A computer can provide you with a wide range of different screen colours. If a colour printer is available you may be able to print these onto design sheets or even directly onto certain graphic products. Beware though – simpler computer programs and printers do not match print colours to those on screen.

The colours of this prototype fragrance box were printed directly onto the net from a computer.

1 On your way home from school look at street signs. Record which ones are most eye-catching or easily seen from a distance. Analyse and compare the colours of two of them to explain why this is so.

2 Analyse a poster or sign to explain why certain colours have been used. Start by comparing the colours used with your own colour swatches and then explain why you think the main colours chosen are suited to their purpose.

3 Look at pictures of interiors in magazines and on paint-sample brochures. Analyse your own emotional response to colours used for different rooms. Give an example of what you think is:

- a restful colour scheme
- a lively colour scheme.

Layout

The images that we receive are usually well planned and targeted. This of course relies on both the graphic images and text. However, the way that the text and images are arranged together has a powerful influence on how effective the graphic product is. Layout or composition are the technical terms used for these considerations in graphics.

For an effective layout you will need to consider the **size**, **position** and **orientation** of each part of your design and how they interact with each other.

Working with text and images

Text and graphic images on a single piece of work can be laid out in an endless variety of ways. Products that serve the same purpose can also be treated in quite different ways. Of course, when you consider the layout of text it will also influence the choice of typeface, style and size. Areas of text can also be aligned in different ways – ranged left, ranged right, justified and centred. Text can also be very irregular and informal – a common method of adding impact.

 Lettering, page 33

Images can also vary enormously in style and subject matter. They too can be handled differently by the designer. They could be cut out, formally squared-up or have a border (box rule). They could be torn, angled, faded-out, part covered etc.

Ultimately, the relationship between the text and the images is the most important consideration and you must work with both together – not finalise one before starting on the other.

> **Focused task: Analysing layout**
>
> Select a page from a magazine and draw a grid over it, emphasising the main lines and areas it is divided into, to analyse the page layout. Then use this grid to create your own article, but using different images and text. When you have finished, compare it with the original. How similar does it look to the magazine original?

When you are working on a layout, try variations of the following:

◆ formal text and informal images
◆ informal text styles with formal images
◆ increasing the impact of the text (tracing film over the images?)
◆ increasing the impact of the images (air-brush white over the text?).

Paste-up

To play with changes such as these, the most important thing is to avoid committing yourself for as long as possible, so you can try (model) design

Different ways of aligning text.

variations. The way this is done is to cut out each element of a graphic design and move them around, trying different relationships, replacing different parts, until you feel you have the best design possible. Then you paste the parts down to 'freeze' your design. This may then be the finished artwork or may be a finished rough from which you generate the final graphic by working more carefully.

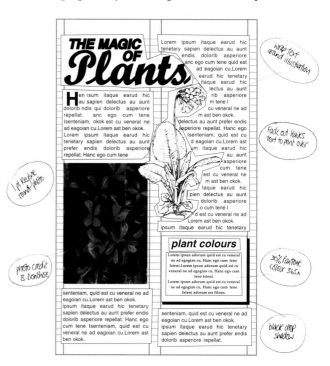

Here is a paste-up which has allowed careful selection and positioning of images and text.

Style

When buying a product, such as a bike, a car or a pair of trainers, we often search for a particular style. What thoughts lie behind our choices? Style is more than a matter of your own taste. As a designer, you will have to consider the style that users of your product, or your target audience, may prefer.

It can be easier to understand the suitability of a style if you prepare a mood board that gives you a set of design clues that all sit well together, giving the 'feel' you want to achieve. Another way is to sum up the style you are aiming for in a few words such as contemporary or classical, elaborate or plain, innovative or traditional, rural or chic, depending on what is needed. Look-up 'Military' and 'Post-modernist' styles in the *D&T Routes Core Book*, page 73.

Rendering

At primary school you may have talked about 'colouring-in' a drawing. The proper term for this is **rendering** and this is concerned with making a drawing look more realistic, by adding colour and other surface effects such as **grain** and **texture**. Rendered drawings can give a highly realistic impression of a product and are often used by designers to communicate an idea to a client. They can also be very seductive so can be used to mislead a client. This has sometimes been the case in architecture for example, where a design looked really good on paper but seemed far too large or dull when built. However, designers need to communicate to their clients what a product will look like, if they are to gain approval to go ahead. Rendered drawings as well as 3D models are vital for this, whether created by hand or on a computer.

A rendered drawing often takes a long time, so is usually only produced in the later stages of designing as a final model – like a prototype. Sometimes though, a designer will work immediately with colour to produce high quality 'roughs' for immediate feedback from their client. Spirit markers are often used for this.

Before you can produce rendered drawings you will need a line drawing on which to work. This could be an orthographic or pictorial view, whichever is

the most appropriate. When preparing a drawing for rendering avoid heavy black outlines which may confuse the finished piece. Make a drawing with a soft pencil, which can be erased or lined later, or make a pencil copy if the original is an ink drawing.

Materials and equipment needed for rendering

Rendering requires a line drawing to be filled and detailed so that a feeling of solidity and reality is achieved. Although some graphics materials are expensive, good effects can be achieved at minimum cost by using more familiar colouring media including:

pencils	paints – such as water colours
charcoal or pastel	and designers' gouache
dry transfers	pens, felt-tips, fibre-tips and
coloured inks	spirit markers
airbrushes	

Computer applications such as Autocad and Corel Draw can be used to produce coloured drawings but fully detailed rendering requires very expensive software, often involving more than one application program. See the packaging example on page 50 for an example of this.

The range of effects available can be increased by mixing the media, perhaps by applying one over the top of another, e.g. coloured pencil over marker. You will need to practice because some materials and colours work better together than others.

This example used markers for the base colours, where large spaces needed to be filled, and white gouache paint to show reflective 'highlights'. A similar affect can be achieved using white coloured pencil (preferably a water-soluble *aquarelle*) but the contrast will not be so dramatic.

Rendering

Selecting your paper

The paper you use will have a significant effect on the results you get. Some graphics media behave very differently on different papers.

If you intend rendering with the special spirit-based felt-tipped pens that graphic designers use (known as markers) you will need to use the right type of paper to control the rate that the ink spreads. For finished work use special **bleed-proof paper** which is treated to prevent the ink giving a blurred, or fuzzy, image. Always use a paper that is not too absorbent.

⚠️ Safety note

These pens can give off toxic fumes. Take care, use them in a well-ventilated area and follow the instructions on them.

Spirit-based markers being used on bleed-proof marker paper.

You can use a fineliner (or fibre-tip pen) to outline your image before you use markers, but make sure it is the waterproof type so that the pigment doesn't get smudged into the coloured areas.

The type of paper, or **ground**, on which you work will affect the appearance of your rendering with other media too. If you can, experiment with a range of different papers before making your final choice.

Soft graphite (6B to B) and coloured pencils work much better on a coarse textured paper with plenty of **tooth** – too smooth a paper will give a very unpleasant result. Almost all papers have a front and back – the latter is rougher and is often better for rendering work. You may find that a dark background paper colour makes your rendering appear brighter.

Like markers, water colours give very different results depending on the absorbency of the paper.

Light and shade

Rendering requires an understanding of light and shade. This is determined both by the amount of light and its source (where it comes from). Those areas nearest to the light source will be lightest and those furthest away darkest. In between there may be several distinct tones. By introducing light and shade a drawing is given **depth**.

The surface nearest to the light source is highlighted – especially if the surface of the object is highly reflective.

Adding shadows to your rendering may improve its **realism**. They are always cast away from the light source and you will need to think carefully about where they should be placed. Tracing the shadows back to the light source will show you that their edges converge.

Textures

Using textures to show different materials can help your rendered drawings to look more realistic. Textures increase the feeling of depth and help the viewer to see what materials the object is made from.

Focused task: Rendering

Draw three small toys from home, made from different materials. Using coloured pencils colour, shade and texture your drawings so that you can tell which materials the toys are made from.

Nets and packaging

Nets, sometimes referred to as **developments**, are the two-dimensional shapes needed for cutting from flat sheet material and folding into three-dimensional products. They are necessary when designing such objects as packages, metal boxes and lamps. They can be surprisingly complex, even for products which in their final form look quite simple.

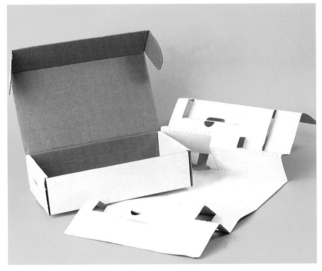

Look how complex the net is for the liner which supported the product contained in this simple rectangular box.

Packaging has at least two major purposes: to **protect**, and to **inform** people about, the contents. Sometimes one of these is much more important than the other. For example, a transport crate might be almost wholly for protective purposes with simple stencilling on it to say what it contains. Alternatively, fancy decorative packaging can be a main reason why some products such as perfumes sell better than their competition. Some contents need little protection but their packages are needed as containers, and perhaps dispensers, for example washing-up liquid.

Consumer products are usually packaged for protection in transit or in use and decorated to attract people to them, help sell them and inform shops and users about their contents. Sometimes the package also acts as a **point-of-sale display** opening out to display the products inside when in a shop.

> ## Focused task: Disassembling packages
>
> The best way to understand nets is to take some apart or disassemble them. Unpick some card packages of different shapes and sizes and lay them flat on a table to see their nets. This is something you can do at home so you can compare everyone's results back at school. Try to understand every single feature of the net: look at how they glue or lock together, how folds are made easier, whether there are access holes for fingers etc.

Designing a net, so that the packaging works as intended, is challenging. This includes considering the final form, how the package protects its contents, assembly method and strength in use. You must consider how the box will fit together, as well as where each surface will end up when folded.

In an attempt to create visual interest and attract people's attention, graphic designers are employed to invent novel packages. In recent years there has been a huge increase in the variety and design of packaging with shapes that can be surprising and unusual.

These packages needed more complex nets and required special folding machines to construct but they help sell their contents as well as protecting them.

Nets require accurate geometrical drawing and a lot of modelling to ensure that they will work well. Paper is fine for early models but prototypes need to be made in materials the same as or nearer to the final package.

DESIGNING

Case study: *Wind-eze packaging*

The drawing and artwork on the opposite page show a pack for Setlers Wind-eze tablets from the London design consultancy Webb Scarlett. The annotations are explained in the key below. The pack can be seen in 3D mock-up form in the photograph.

The first stage of the design of the pack was to decide on a suitable packaging format. In this case a blister pack within a relatively simple six-sided card box was chosen.

A net was then created – in the packaging industry this is called a cutter guide. When designing the cutter guide many things needed to be considered. Primarily the box had to work when folded up with tabs in the correct places etc. Other more complex issues included the efficient use of materials and the strength of the pack. For example, a box usually has its openings along its short sides. This normally means the box will use up less material (it is possible to get more of them out of a sheet of card) and will also be stronger, as the folds run down the long sides. Notice also how the seam and the pack openings are positioned to ensure that the cut edges of the card are at the back of the pack. This means the pack will have a clean front face presented to the customer when it is on the shelf.

Artwork was then designed and laid onto the cutter guide. Care was taken to ensure that the graphics on each face were correctly orientated, so they appear the right way up when the pack is constructed.

As Setlers Wind-eze tablets are a pharmaceutical product, there was a great deal of statutory copy that was legally required to be included on the pack. These included 'Keep out of reach of children', and the name and quantity of the active ingredient 'Simethicone USP 125mg – wind disperser' which had to appear on every visible face of the pack.

Cutter guide
Glue area   shaded or hatched
Cut lines   drawn as solid lines
Locking tabs hold the ends closed and prevent them from being pushed into the box
Fold lines   drawn as dotted lines

Artwork
Statutory copy legally required information
Violator   designed to stand out and grab attention
                         'NEW!' can only remain on the pack for one year
Glue area   left unprinted so glue will adhere better
Copyright   © and ® symbols used to protect brand names from being copied
Bar code   space for a standard bar code
Bleed   minimum 3 mm of colour printed beyond the cutter guides to allow for slight
                         inaccuracies
Expiry date   space for the manufacturer to stamp the expiry date of the tablets
Window   reflecting the shape of part of the logo, showing a tablet; windows must not be
                         too close to fold lines

Fold lines

Locking tabs

Glue area

Cut lines

Violator

Statutory copy

Setlers® Wind-eze®
Express Relief from the Pain of Trapped Wind

Tamper Resistant Package
If foil on inner package is broken, do not use.

SIMETHICONE USP 125mg - WIND DISPERSER

NEW! *CHEWABLE*

Setlers®

Wind-eze®

SIMETHICONE USP 125mg - WIND DISPERSER

EXPRESS RELIEF
From the Pain of Trapped Wind

10
PEPPERMINT TABLETS

10 CHEWABLE PEPPERMINT TABLETS

Setlers® Wind-eze®
Express Relief from the Pain of Trapped Wind

SIMETHICONE USP 125mg - WIND DISPERSER

Setlers®

Wind-eze®

SIMETHICONE USP 125mg - WIND DISPERSER

Use for: Relief from the symptoms of stomach pain and bloating due to the presence of trapped wind.

Dosage: 1 or 2 tablets to be taken 3 or 4 times daily (or as required for relief of symptoms) after meals and at bedtime. The tablets must be chewed before swallowing. Not recommended for children under 12 years.
Do not use Setlers Wind-eze for more than 14 days without medical advice.

Warnings & Precautions: The product should not be used in patients with known hypersensitivity to any of the ingredients.
Do not exceed the stated dose.
If you take too many tablets, or your symptoms persist or worsen, or you experience any undesirable effects with this product, seek medical advice.
Since simethicone is not absorbed by the body, there are no contra-indications to its use during pregnancy and breast feeding. However, as with all medicines, ask your doctor or pharmacist for advice before taking this product.

Keep out of reach of children.

Symptoms of stomach pain and bloating can be caused by the build up of trapped wind. Setlers Wind-eze is specifically formulated to relieve these symptoms by gently dispersing the tiny bubbles of trapped wind without risk of embarrassment.

Active ingredient: Each chewable tablet contains Simethicone USP 125mg - Wind Disperser.

Also contains: Starch, sorbitol, tribasic calcium phosphate, citric acid, talc, peppermint flavour, non-pareil seeds (sugar and starch).

Product licence holder:
Stafford-Miller Ltd.,
Broadwater Road, Welwyn
Garden City, Herts AL7 3SP
PL 0036 / 0084
Date of last revision: June 96

Setlers and Wind-eze are Registered
Trademarks of Stafford-Miller Ltd.
© STAFFORD-MILLER LTD 1996

Store below 25°C in a dry place.
Do not use after expiry date shown on pack and blister foil.
Manufactured by:
Wrafton Laboratories Ltd., Wrafton, Braunton, N.Devon EX33 2DL

0505072013

Glue area

Bar code

Copyright

Bleed

Expiry date

Window

designed by **WEBB SCARLETT** DESIGN FOR BRANDS

2D graphics and 3D form

One of the complexities of packaging design is that printing on the flat net has to work well when folded into the final 3D form. There are other kinds of graphic products that need a three-dimensional surface if they are to work as intended. This can offer particular opportunities and challenges for the designer.

The moving surfaces of the three-dimensional advertisement hoarding in the photograph below use control systems to increase the quality of the graphic image and the power of the message. Its movements catch the eye.

Some three-dimensional graphic products are more specialised. Road signs and traffic equipment are examples of this.

Case study: Graphic images on 3D

Students at George Ward School, in Wiltshire, used a variety of surplus cardboard boxes to explore ways in which graphic images could be wrapped around 3D forms.

Using an overhead projector, the effect of applying graphic images on these 3D forms was explored.

This 3D advert hoarding in a busy London street gives a novel effect to passers by. It is also very cost-effective because a new image is shown every 20 seconds by revolving sections bringing a new poster to the front.

In the **control part** of this graphic product the **input** is electrical energy, the **output** is rotational movement. The **processing** is done electrically to switch an electric motor on and off in the correct sequence.

Systems and control, page 72

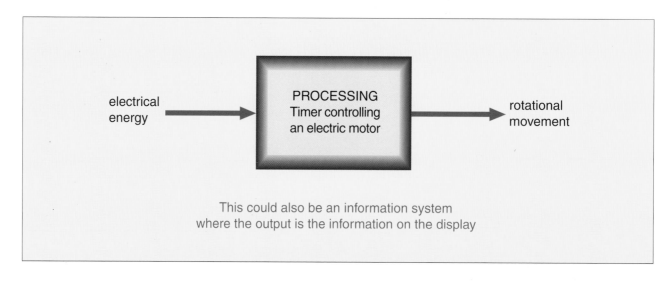

electrical energy → PROCESSING Timer controlling an electric motor → rotational movement

This could also be an information system where the output is the information on the display

Computer graphics

Ways in which computers can assist you in designing and making graphic products are mentioned frequently in this book.

A computer is a tool which, like any other tool, when used appropriately may lead to an improved product or a more convenient way for you to work. There are also times when more traditional methods are better than computers for the task in hand. For example over-using images from **clip-art** files stops you creating your own new and original ideas.

Do the right thing!

- Do try to use computer applications on D&T tasks to expand your IT experience.
- Do use them when they might lead to better results.
- Do always consider the traditional alternative in case it has advantages.
- Don't use them just to avoid developing other skills.

Computers in the graphics industry

The last ten years have brought extraordinary changes to the way that graphic designers work. Traditionally, illustrations and text would have been more labour intensive, done by hand taking a great deal of time. Most graphic designers now use computers all the time with specialist software for text, hand-drawn images, altering photographic images and bringing these together to make-up pages (desktop publishing).

Using such software designers can:

- ◆ import text from word-processors
- ◆ import images from other devices like scanners and digital cameras
- ◆ edit their work repeatedly – until they and the client are happy
- ◆ automate repetitive tasks – like forming columns and dividing pages into boxes of text and pictures
- ◆ create and adapt images by manipulating texture, colour, scale and proportion; rotating, mirroring and distorting them.

Case study: Designing computer games boxes

Creative Advertising and Print Ltd design and print computer games boxes for companies like Sony, Sega and Nintendo.

Originally, computer games boxes were illustrated by hand, using air-brushing techniques.

The company work in the specialist computer games market where highly visual packaging is needed to catch the vivid imaginations of young customers. The design of the boxes has now moved off the traditional drawing board to 95% of it being done on computers.

The designers need creative skills in illustration and design and technical skill in desktop publishing. 'The level of innovation demanded in the games business is enormous,' says director Roger Pearse, 'and communication is the key to good design. To understand the brief and solve it successfully you must also understand what is to be said, how to say it and who to say it to.' In other words know your **target audience**.

Data from a computer-aided design file can be easily converted into a product using computer-aided manufacturing methods, or CAD/CAM. The designs for these Sony, Sega and Nintendo boxes can be designed and printed in-house without the need for any hands-on illustration.

Adding digital images to the design

Importing images, such as photographs or video-stills, to form part of a design is now very common. The photo or other image may be scanned by a device which converts it into digital signals that the computer can read. The images can then be further developed on screen and stored for future use.

Digital stills

The digital video stills camera, know as DVS, is becoming much cheaper and is being used in a lot of schools. It allows images to be captured on disk and imported directly into a design or desktop-publishing computer program and it involves no recurrent costs for film.

The user can create and record images, loading them directly from the camera into the computer, without the need for processing into paper prints beforehand.

A school's DVS camera

Most DVS cameras can record and store between 40–70 good quality images at any one time. Composing your image is the same as for film based cameras. For you to do this, you will first need to be clear about the equipment and facilities available. You will need a DVS camera as well as a computer program, such as Corel Draw, into which your digital stills can be imported.

Whether identifying a need or choosing DVS to help develop your design, it will help you to evaluate some existing products that have been created in this way beforehand.

Working in a digital design environment

Most designers will use several different programmes to develop their designs. More powerful computers will allow you to have two or three of these software applications running simultaneously. This means that an image can be modified in one program and then imported into or updated in another.

Some programs have pre-designed layouts, or templates, which may be specifically designed for such things as CD covers, video sleeves and magazine page formats. These can greatly simplify and speed-up the process of designing.

Stop and think

- How important are these new methods of designing with computer graphics, compared with hand methods?
- What are the main skills these designers need?
- Do you think that designers will need to be computer technicians?
- Is it still necessary for these designers to be able to draw?
- Importing an image (like 'sampling' music) can be seen as stealing from the person who created it. Should this be illegal? Should fees be paid to the originators?
- Some people say that traditional hand methods are no longer needed because computers have made it so easy to form graphics and text on screen. What is your view?
- What would happen if two powerful companies found themselves using the same image in their adverts?
- If every designer uses computers, who will teach today's students to draw? Could these skills be lost and does it matter?

Sequencing information

There are times when imparting information graphically requires it to be delivered in a careful sequence. A commonly used technique for working out such sequences is **storyboarding**.

Literally, storyboarding means telling a story using pictures and words on a series of boards. The **boards** are usually small boxes in order on sheets of paper and this method is commonly used in television and advertising. Storyboards allow the designer to explain the plot, or story, so that detailed design decisions can be made for screen production.

Focused task: Using a storyboard as a planning tool

- Find out the title and theme of a film on TV this week.
- Create an **ident** (introductory logo) for the company sponsoring this film. Make a storyboard, consisting of drawn pictures and words, to illustrate the main steps in the story. Make a rough outline first and discuss it with someone else who has seen the film.
- Test your storyboard by getting a group of fellow students to follow it. Ask them if they can follow the story.

①  ②

③  ④

⑤  ⑥

⑦

This storyboard was created by M&C Saatchi to plan a television advertisement for Currys.

The storyboard is an important **planning** tool. It is drawn in a quick visual style, not unlike a cartoon, and used before production starts. All design teams involved in the production, including set design, props, effects, lighting and make up, will use it.

Communicating numbers graphically

Numerical data, although of great importance, can be very boring and difficult to understand if presented just as numbers. Displaying it graphically can make data easier to understand and have an impact on the target audience.

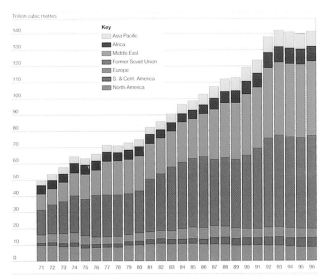

A designer turned this information on world reserves of natural gas into a graphic product, making the key trends clearer.

Graphic designers often present such data to a variety of audiences using visual images to liven-up the display and draw attention to the parts that they wish to stress.

Communicating numbers graphically

Displaying quantitative data in school

There are many opportunities to design and make this type of graphic product in school.

Most presentations of quantitative data are now done using computer graphics, often linked with spreadsheet software. Presentations can be extremely eye-catching and clever, particularly when they include multi-media applications such as animation, background video sequences and sound.

Values issues

Could there be a problem when presentations of serious information become very attractive and entertaining?

Could the data be distorted through the way it has been presented? If you were expected to deliberately distort data would you feel guilty about this? How do you think designers cope with such conflicts?

Focused task: Formulating a specification

1 Find three examples of graphically presented data from newspapers or magazines and turn them back into a list of numbers.

2 Now draw a graph using the same numbers but distorting them to mislead the 'reader'.

Explain, with notes attached:

■ who is your target audience?
■ what message(s) do you intend your graphic product to convey?

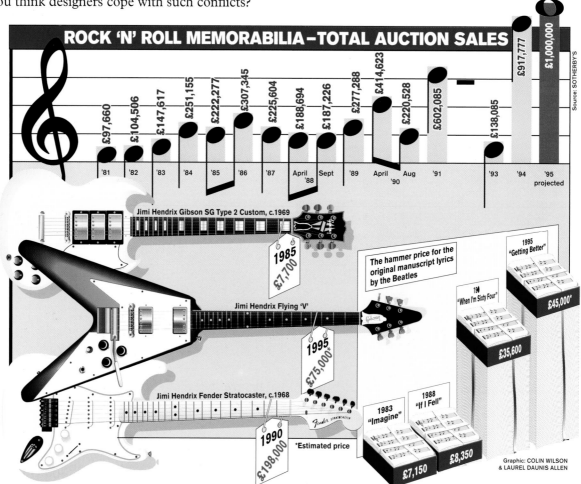

A computer-generated image from the Mail on Sunday newspaper.

DESIGNING

Using graphics to instruct and inform

Finding your way around

Graphic products are ideal for giving people information to help them find their way around. When in unfamiliar surroundings a map is a very useful graphic product. Some maps are realistic, or show detailed features exactly, while other kinds are representative and only show what the viewer needs to know.

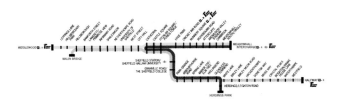

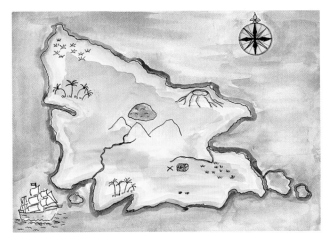

Maps can be realistic or representative as long as they can be understood.

Maps can be very complex or simple and diagrammatic. More information is included on topographical maps (that attempt to describe the landscape) than road maps. But even maps that are focused on helping people find one place can be difficult to design.

Focused task: Maps

Draw a map with as little text information as possible, to help someone find a particular book in your school library, starting from where you are now. Test your map design on independent users. Compare with others how you solved the problem.

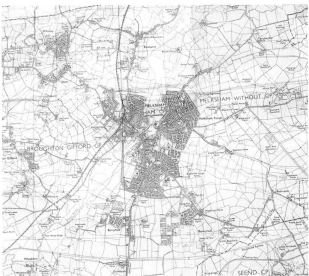

A topographical map can give more information allowing you to identify land marks, hills and valleys.

Signposts are another way in which graphic design helps people find their way around. Road signs and those in complex buildings like hospitals and schools need to be clear and to give the most useful information. They need to be easy and quick to read and so need their colour, typeface, size, shape, style and positioning to be carefully determined. This can be a challenging graphic design task.

Instructional graphics

A map is an example of non-verbal, and in this case graphic, communication being used to explain or inform. Some kinds of graphic communication have to work in any situation, or be universal, especially if they impart information to people who speak different languages.

There are many examples of instructional graphics and they can sometimes mean the difference between life and death.

 Survival DMA, page 4

Using graphics to instruct and inform

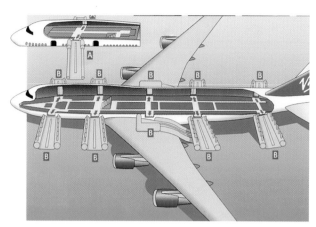

These universal safety instructions are designed to work quickly.

Instructional graphics can be used to explain how to assemble or use a product.

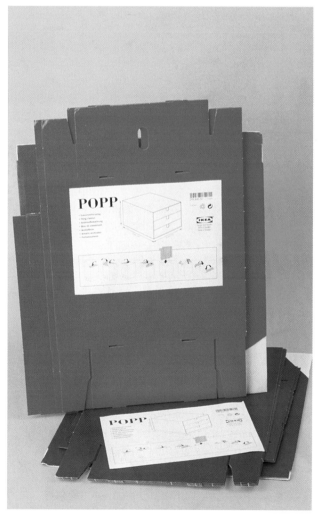

These drawer units from IKEA include the instructional graphics needed to assemble them as intended.

Instructional graphics often involve a sequence of operations like a storyboard.

You must also consider:

- ◆ style of drawing (page 47)
- ◆ scale (page 41)
- ◆ arrows – which need designing very carefully – use paste-up for trials
- ◆ insets – small details added in a separate box
- ◆ where to focus attention
- ◆ where and whether to add detail
- ◆ where and whether to reduce detail.

style of drawing (page 47); scale (page 41)

Focused task: Information graphics

There are many examples of graphic products which instruct or inform. You can practise designing and making products of this kind, as well as trying them out to see how well they perform.

1 Design a directional sign that will work for sighted and visually impaired users. The sign must work both visually and by feel, using a tactile element. Your sign will also have to work for all directions including up and down stairs. You can choose your own application such as a sign that shows the way to the emergency exits in an hotel.

2 Design a set of instructional graphics for a hot-glue gun that can be printed onto the side of the gun to show how to replace the glue stick. Space is limited and you will only be able to use three or four steps. Think about how you will need to hold the product to view the instructions whilst carrying out the replacement.

Fasten the grip belt
- Release the Velcro fastening and hold the camera with your right hand while you adjust the belt with your left.

Adjust the viewfinder
- Adjust the viewfinder to suit your eyesight by turning the viewfinder focusing ring until the viewfinder displays are clearly focused. First put the camera in record pause mode (turn the OPERATE switch to CAMERA and set the STANDBY/LOCK switch to STANDBY).
- The viewfinder rotates through 90° to give a choice of shooting positions.

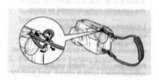

Attach the shoulder strap
- For extra security and portability, attach the shoulder strap before using the camera.
- Pass the ends through the attachment bars and adjust the length as shown.

The designer of this instructional leaflet had to think about the orientation of the camera when being held by the user.

Thinking about . . .

Materials when designing

Graphic products are often made from paper and boards (card). There is an enormous variety of these, though schools can usually only provide a very limited range. You will have to consider what you will use for your products. For major projects you should expect to have to buy more specialist materials. The notes below should help you make your design decisions.

Paper and boards come in a variety of sizes, colours, weights and finishes. The most common sizes are in the metric system: A0, A1, A2, A3, A4 etc. These derive from A0 being a square metre in area with each size in turn being a half of the area of the one before. B sizes are A sizes with an extra border and C and D sizes are available for special applications like envelopes. Boards come in a confusing range of sizes based on traditions from various industries – different types often come in different sizes!

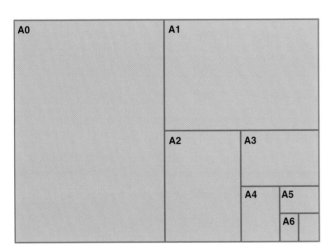

Metric paper sizes.

The most common plain paper in schools is **bond**. Thinner than this is **bank** paper which is similar to **layout** paper, which designers use as a semi-tracing film with a smooth surface.

Weight: is a measure of a paper's thickness and is measured by the number of grams per square metre (gsm). For example, most photocopies are on 80 gsm whereas a higher quality letter paper might be 120 gsm.

Laminates, like plywood and tin plate, many boards are built-up from layers, some giving strength, some the desired surface. Specialist applications include aluminium layers to ensure that a package is water-tight. It is quite possible for you to glue together different layers (laminates) to achieve the performance that is required as long as you press them together well when gluing.

Surface finishes: papers such as cartridge can be rough surfaced through being allowed to dry naturally when first laid down (in pulp form). Or they can be polished by spinning rollers or given a shiny top laminate.

Special surface treatments include: high quality stationery being **embossed** to give raised lettering or logos (you can do that); menu cards in restaurants being **coated** with plastic film to make them easy to clean and glossy finishes applied to expensive brochures to make them look and feel stronger and more attractive.

The special layers in Tetrapak material allow the product to stay fresh and prevent the cardboard container from leaking.

Thinking about . . .

Legal requirements

You should include relevant regulations and controls in your design specification.

When testing and evaluating graphic products such as posters with a powerful message or meaning, you may need to check against regulations or **codes of practice**. It would probably be too costly and time consuming to obtain independent feedback from a regulatory body. However you could form your own panel, asking a variety of people from different backgrounds to look at your product. Their feedback could help you to avoid causing unnecessary offence.

Some products are affected by legal requirements or standards. The following is a general guide which you can use to help build your specification. You can see some specific examples in the packaging case study on page 50.

Copyright

All existing drawings, photographs, illustrations and text are covered by copyright. However, **ideas** can not be copyrighted, only the actual designs. Copyright means that the piece of work belongs to somebody and cannot be used without their permission, you do *not* have the right to copy it. One common example of this is when you want to use cartoon characters as part of your design.

Mickey Mouse, for example, belongs to the Walt Disney Corporation and cannot be used for commercial production without their permission. In practice, this means that they might licence its use but would probably charge a fee as part of a licensing agreement.

Packaging legislation

Two thirds of all packaging is used to protect food products and so there is considerable legislation to help ensure our health and safety. Staff at the Packaging Industry Research Association (PIRA) set standards to avoid the wrong materials being used to package food products. You may be unable to find out about such regulations affecting your design but should try your best to track them down.

Food labelling

A label may help to decorate, identify, inform and promote a product. Labels used by the food and drink industries are controlled by the Food Labelling Regulations, 1984, which help to protect the consumer.

Foods which are ready for delivery to the customer or to a catering establishment must be marked with:

- The name of the food – not just a brand name, fancy name or trademark.
- A list of ingredients, including permitted additives, shown in descending order by weight.
- An indication of the minimum durability expressed in terms of day, month, year. A "best before" and "use by" should be given with perishable goods.
- Any special storage requirements or conditions of use.
- The name or business name and address or registered office of the manufacturer, packer or seller within the EEC.
- Place of origin of the food, if lack of such information could materially mislead the consumer.
- Instructions for preparation if necessary.

This kind of legislation is used to regulate the words, trade marks, brand names, pictorial matter and symbols relating to the food.

Specifications: D&T Routes Core Book, pages 49, 106, 147

Advertising

You should not make claims for products or services which you cannot fully justify. *Legal, decent, honest and truthful* is the common slogan which is used to guide advertising.

A special code of conduct is monitored by the Advertising Standards Authority (ASA). Briefly, this means that an advert should not:

◆ encourage or appear to approve of illegal or criminal acts
◆ cause grave or widespread offence to the standards of decency of those likely to see it
◆ make claims which cannot be verified – words like "best", "finest" should only be used when they are likely to be understood as obvious exaggeration
◆ mislead the consumer
◆ misuse scientific research or data to make exaggerated claims for the product.

The British Code of Advertising Practice (BCAP), says that in addition to the items above, advertisers should follow business principles of fair competition and be responsible to the consumers and society. This general code of conduct is also worth considering when you design packaging as this is a form of advertising.

Values issues

Graphic products are often designed to carry powerful meanings or messages. It may be difficult for us to avoid exposure to them and, whether we like it or not, we can become involved or form opinions as a result.

◆ Is this a good thing?
◆ Should we be protected from false or misleading information or should we be allowed to make our own judgement about such things?

WITHDRAWN

X

If an ad misleads, we're here to stamp it out.
Advertising Standards Authority
2 Torrington Place London WC1E 7HW 0171 580 5555 http://www.asa.org.uk **ASA**

Thinking about . . .

Design for manufacture

Is your design intended for manufacture in **high volumes** or do you intend to make a **single item**? Making this choice will affect many fundamental design decisions.

 D&T Routes Core Book, Design for Manufacture, page 103

Items that are hand crafted are limited mainly by your own personal skills, time and the materials and equipment available to you. Manufacturing in large quantities needs a different approach.

The shape, colour, material and complexity of your design may be governed by a range of factors set out in your brief and detailed in a design specification. In particular, you will need to anticipate:

◆ the kind of equipment and machinery needed for repeated production
◆ the total quantity of material needed for a large number of products
◆ labour, including numbers of people and the level of skills that they need
◆ the time that it will take for a paid workforce to carry out manufacture.

Being able to make repeat items reliably, including such things as size, shape, colour and finish, will mean using special tools, such as jigs. **Quality control systems** will also be needed to maintain standards.

 D&T Routes Core Book, Quality Control, pages 131, 153

Use this chart to help you consider different processes and methods of construction.

Process category	Examples
paste-ups	photocopying and clip-art
fabrication	cutting, folding, joining, vinyl cutting
cardboard engineering	machinery, mechanisms, pop-ups
using press knives	volume production of pressed shapes
assembly	gluing, assembly of sheet materials
printing	block and screen printing
finishing	surface-coatings and embossing

Case study: *Two birthday cards compared*

One of these cards is

■ individually designed to be made as a one-off item
■ hand-embroidered
■ slightly padded
■ of a non-standard size therefore requiring a hand-made envelope
■ three times the cost of the other.

The other card is

■ designed with a potential print-run of 100,000 copies
■ flat, for easy printing, cutting, packing and display
■ a standard size, chosen for economical use of paper
■ designed to fit a standard envelope and shop-display stand
■ printed on a standard card material for easy availability and reduced cost
■ printed using **lithography**, a printing process suited to efficient, high volume production.

The individually-crafted card costs three times as much as the high-volume card. It might be purchased for a special person, or for a more important birthday, with extra quality in mind.

Focused task: Formulating a specification

1 Get the worksheet 'Volume Production' from your teacher and compare the two birthday cards using both the headings on the worksheet and the points mentioned above.

2 Create a model of a greeting card that you think might be suitable for high volume production. Use cuttings from magazines and text from your computer to create a product that could be printed full colour outside and one colour inside. Make a presentation to some fellow students and explain why your card is suitable for high volume production.

DESIGNING

Costs and prices

The *D&T Routes Core Book* shows in detail (pages 74–75) how to calculate total product costs and that they are a serious consideration for you.

Being clear about your budget

Budget considerations are very important to the success of any product. Graphic designers often charge by the hour and will be expected to quote on how much a job will cost, normally having to stick to that price, even if the job takes longer than originally anticipated.

From the client's point of view there are other budget constraints to be taken into consideration; for example how many colours will be available for printing or, in the case of large displays, the materials needed in fabrication. All of these factors would be discussed at the briefing meetings between designer and client. Once all these things have been decided the designer can start to plan the project.

Manufacturing costs and the selling price

Even when the cost of developing and producing a product are calculated thoroughly, setting the price may still be a difficult decision. Quite often, manufacturers of graphic products are working to a price that has already been fixed and must make sure that their overheads, including the time that a project is taking, allow them an adequate profit.

 The business of manufacturing, page 90

You too need to work out the expected costs involved in your product in advance or you may get a shock. And you may need to set a price, if you are interested in sales.

Do the right thing!

What are your product costs? Use the diagram below, together with information from the *D&T Routes Core Book*, to calculate your own product's costs.

- Could different manufacturing methods help you reduce your costs?
- If so, would you pass on all of these savings to the customer?
- What might be the effect of competition on your pricing decisions?

what is left over when the expenses have been paid — **Profit** — e.g. The amount left of the selling price after all of the expenses have been paid

Non-production overheads — e.g. Rent charged on the warehouse, shops, some people's wages, advertising

The expenses that are caused by making the ice-lolly — **Production overheads** — e.g. Cost of keeping the lollies frozen, warehousing, transport to the shops

Prime costs — e.g. The cost of what is actually used to make the ice-lolly, including water, sugar, colouring, flavouring, electricity for freezing the ice, the stick, the wrapper and all the wages paid to the people who actually make the lolly

The best price is the one that generates a maximum profit for the company, and not necessarily the one that sells the most products.

MANUFACTURING

This section will help you with questions about manufacturing, particularly if you are making more than one item and manufacturing in volume. Products that you make in school may be **one-offs**, or prototypes with batch or high volume production in mind. Even if you cannot put your ideas into large scale production, knowing how manufacturing industry produces products will help you to make appropriate decisions. It is also important that you come to understand how the many industrial products around you come into being.

You will need to consider how you can manufacture your product(s) to the quality that is needed and, if you are planning volume production, how your methods will differ from one-off production.

Keeping a systems overview

Whatever your scale of production you can improve your work by using a systematic approach.

> **D&T Routes Core Book,**
> **Manufacturing as a system,**
> **page 118**

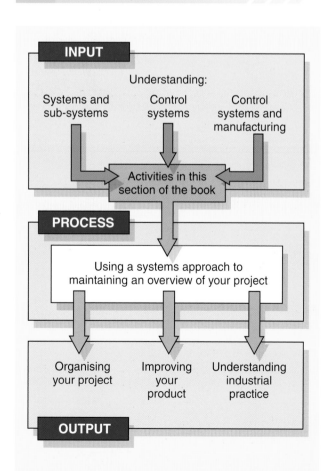

Keeping a systems overview of your product can help you to:

- ◆ better organise and carry out your manufacturing
- ◆ maintain and improve the quality of your product as it develops
- ◆ understand industrial manufacturing practices.

Organising manufacturing

Whether you are planning one-off production or producing more than one graphic product, comparing your approach with industrial methods will improve your knowledge and understanding of manufacturing. You will also find that it will help you to be more systematic in your work.

Planning production

There is a great deal in the *D&T Routes Core Book* (pages 126–143) to help you plan your production, so it is worth checking in it regularly.

When choosing materials or processing methods from those covered in this section remember to think about the volume of production you intend, the material available and the quality of the final product that you require.

Health and safety

You will need to consider health and safety issues when working in the graphics area. Again you should refer to 'Health & Safety' in the *D&T Routes Core Book*, but paying special attention to the following will further help prevent accidents in this area.

Do the right thing!

When working with cutting tools:

- check the equipment is in good order
- protect yourself by using a safety rule and mat
- protect others working nearby
- dispose of sharp objects with care
- take your time and work with great care.

When spraying inks, glues or paints:

- protect yourself and your clothing
- extract the fumes or over-spray
- ensure there is good ventilation
- protect surfaces near to you
- wait for the object to dry
- clean up after yourself to prevent damage to others, work or the equipment.

Manufacturing processes

Many different manufacturing processes could be needed for your product. Because a graphic product can be made in almost any material you may need to consult the other books in the *D&T Routes* series as the need arises: *Resistant Materials*, *Textiles*, *Food* and *Control Products* as well as the *Core Book*.

Manufacturing from a paste-up model

When designing a layout you will have considered the size, position and orientation of each part of your design and may have used paste-ups to develop your design.

 Layout, page 45

If your graphic product is to be produced in a small batch, or limited print-run of not more than 500 copies, your final paste-up might become the **master copy** from which your school photocopier, or other output device, could print.

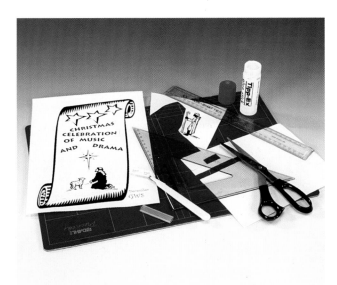

A pasted-up flyer for a limited print-run of 400.

Pasting text and clip-art

A pasted-up master could include a great variety of materials such as text and printed images. You could use a computer database of ready-made shapes, or clip-art, from which selected images could be pasted onto your master.

If using a computer, you could cut and paste your entire master sheet on screen, using page make-up software such as Picture Publisher, Pagemaker, QuarkXpress or Page Plus, without the need for scissors and glue. Screen tools, such as word-wrap, stretch, enlarge and reduce, allow you to finalise your master before final printing.

Fabricating a model or prototype

Manufacturing may involve 2D and 3D prototyping. Materials might include paper, card and others that have more resistant properties. This kind of work is commonly carried out by an industrial model-maker.

An industrial model-maker at work.

Many of the techniques used by industrial model-makers can be carried out in your workshops and graphics areas at school. Most need simple, inexpensive materials and equipment.

Models from card and sheet materials

Card, papers and thin materials come in a variety of forms. You may need to use some of the following hand-working processes.

Cutting and folding

Shapes can easily be marked on paper and card using standard drawing equipment but, if you are working in thin plastic, a marker will probably be needed to make clear lines on a shiny surface. Be careful not to mark out in such a way that the lines cannot be removed after cutting and folding. Neat folds can be achieved in thin materials by scoring – ideally you should cut about half way through the material.

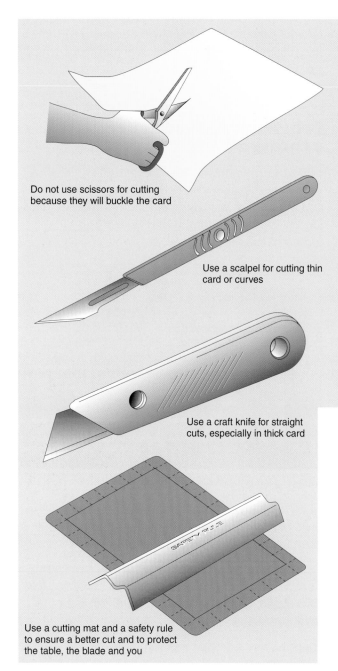

Do not use scissors for cutting because they will buckle the card

Use a scalpel for cutting thin card or curves

Use a craft knife for straight cuts, especially in thick card

Use a cutting mat and a safety rule to ensure a better cut and to protect the table, the blade and you

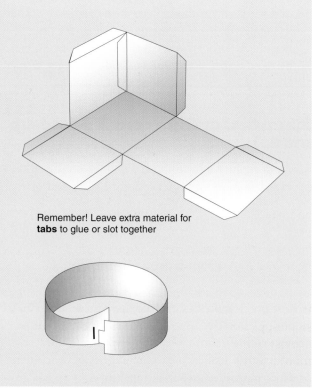

Remember! Leave extra material for **tabs** to glue or slot together

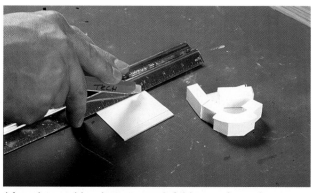

After the card has been scored, fold away from the cut.

Foam board, vacuum-forming plastic sheets, corriflute and cling film can all be used for package models.

Joining

A good adhesive, carefully applied, is the key to a successful join. Often during your course you will use this method to combine and join paper, card and other sheet materials such as corriflute, foamboard and sheet plastics.

You must choose your adhesive carefully, influenced by requirements such as: suitability of the material; strength of join and speed of drying needed.

Methods of joining sheet materials, such as slots and flaps, may require an adhesive to make them permanent. With careful design the join could also be made non-permanent for products that need to be disassembled, or taken apart again.

Sometimes you may need to use a **fixing**, or device to hold sheet materials together. These may include staples, paper fasteners, eyelets, rivets or parts from a construction kit. Joining a complex card model may be easier from a series of simple nets (developments) rather than just one. It may be difficult to work on thin surfaces after a development has been formed. If possible carry out surface decoration beforehand.

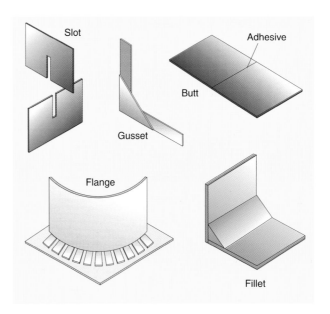

Five possible methods of joining sheet materials.

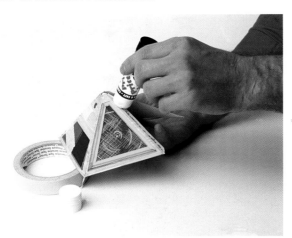

Sticky paper-tape can be used to hold a joint until the main adhesive sets.

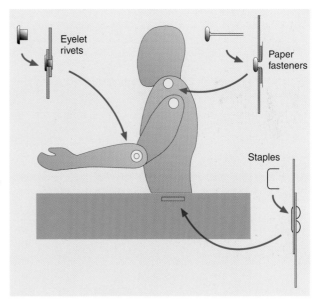

Three possible fixings for joining sheet materials.

ADHESIVES

Type	Use	Advantages and disadvantages	Health and Safety
PVA (e.g. Marvin Medium)	As a strong fixing for card	Very strong Work needs to be held while drying which will take a number of hours PVA may wrinkle papers	Wash hands after use
PVA stick (e.g. PrittStick)	Paper to paper Paper to card	Easy to use Can be messy and picks up dirt	
Latex based adhesives (e.g. Evostick Repositionable, Cow Gum)	Paper to paper Paper to card	Work can be repositioned for a short while after use Excess can be rubbed away with finger	Use in a well ventilated area
Clear adhesives (e.g. UHU, Bostick)	Card to card	Strong with short drying time Must be used carefully to avoid messy edges	
Contact adhesives (e.g. Evostick)	Card to card Many plastics	Very strong bond which is immediate Cannot be repositioned	Use in a well ventilated area
Low-tack adhesives (e.g. BluTack)	Paper to paper Paper to card	Useful for temporary fixing such as to plan a page layout Lumpy nature may show through work Not really repositionable	
Spray mount	Paper to paper Paper to card	Useful for mounting work onto a background Work can be repositioned for a period after use Heavy duty versions available.	Use in a well ventilated area
Double-sided tape	Paper to paper Paper to card Sheet plastics	Clean and easy to use Can be cut to a size appropriate to the work May show through work	
Tensol	Acrylic	Not useful where a high strength join is needed	Avoid contact with skin and eyes and avoid inhalation
Solvent weld	Most varieties of plastics including ABS, polystyrene and acrylic	Clean and neat join Fast acting Different solvents for different materials	Avoid contact with skin and eyes and avoid inhalation
Polystyrene cement	For most forms of polystyrene except foams	Easy to apply from tube	Avoid contact with skin and eyes

Working with foam and more resistant materials

Expanded polystyrene is usually white and lumpy from the expanded beads it is foamed from. **Styrofoam** is usually blue and is finer in texture. Both are very useful modelling materials – they are easy to use and inexpensive but need to be worked skilfully. Harder materials, such as acrylic, hardwoods, MDF and metals, can give an improved finish and allow more detail than card or foam but take more time to work.

Your chosen material will depend on availability, cost and suitability for the task you need to carry out. Making identical shapes can be made easier by using a **template**.

Surface details of models are often built-up, or added-on, rather than cut-away from the solid. Where small gaps appear, these can be filled. Additional trimming and rubbing down may be needed to achieve a good finish.

Foams are soft and easily cut with hot wire and other tools, but be sure that you are working in a well ventilated area.

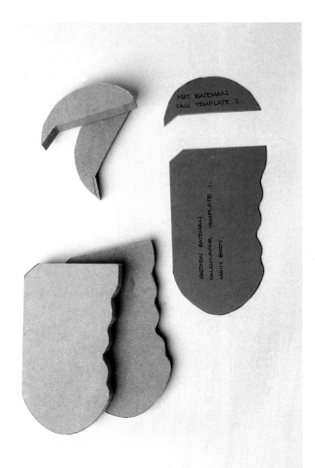

Templates enable you to duplicate identical parts.

Detail is usually added rather than cut-away. A clean, flat base has been made in the recess left for this button panel. Filler can be added to fill gaps or form smooth curves.

Finishing

To obtain a realistic finish your model will need detailed attention and patient work. Once smooth, a foam or other block model can be painted with primer to highlight blemishes that need further work.

Final surface details, including colours, can then be added to the main part of the model. Painting surface details onto components, before attaching them, avoids the need for masking later. This will save time and improve accuracy.

When trimmed and rubbed down with light abrasives until smooth, the model can be given a coat of primer.

Finishing touches bring the model to life and give it extra realism. The buttons have been fully prepared before attachment to avoid painting around them.

Models for film and animation

Some models for products such as film and animation, need to be very detailed and realistic. Programmes such as *Red Dwarf* create a realistic moving image using a series of models to different scales.

Dramatic scenes, such as this, depend on realistic models.

Case study: *The industrial model-maker*

An industrial model-maker sometimes has to create a model that is almost indistinguishable from final production items. A great variety of materials, including more resistant ones, may be needed. Such models may be so complete, in every detail, that they include working features such as electronics.

Image copyright Hayes Davidson

This model of the Millennium Building was needed to communicate information about the design to the public before building and construction decisions could be made.

Models using kits

Mechanical, pneumatic and hydraulic systems are complex and often need to be perfected before production can begin. You may also find them helpful if your graphic product involves using a control system.

Animating control systems, page 76

You may be able to create both model and final product using information technology. For example, **computer-aided design and manufacture** can allow you to view a product before it is made, examine or modify its stages of manufacture as well as provide a realistic final **prototype**. Holding the design information as a computer file means that it can be used repeatedly.

D&T Routes Core Book, Using Computers for Manufacturing, page 132

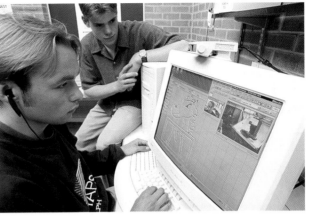

This stylised mustang symbol was designed by students from the United States and England, working as a team with CNC tools.

Computers can also create a **virtual reality (VR) walk-through**, or simulation, of building spaces and interiors giving a feeling of actually being there. Such computer data can be shared between people who may live or work at a distance from each other or for presenting ideas to an audience.

D&T Routes Resistant Materials, Electronic Product Definition, page 57

Type A

These computer-generated VR stills are a kind of graphic product.

Systems and control

Some graphic products use systems to achieve a particular effect.

▶ **D&T Routes Core Book, page 117**

The term **systems and control** covers a range including mechanical, electrical, electro-mechanical, electronic and pneumatic systems. It also covers the use of **control systems** to control these other types of system.

Incorporating some **dynamic** (moving) part, sound or light into your product may enhance it. You can also make the product more interesting by increasing the user's involvement, for example by getting them to operate a trigger or release mechanism.

Using mechanical systems

Mechanical systems include:

◆ levers, linkages, cams, gears and pulleys – these can be used in pop-ups, 3D graphic products and other 'animated' graphic products
◆ electro-mechanical devices such as motors, solenoids, linear actuators (ramrods); pneumatic devices (using syringes and tubing rather than more expensive pneumatics) and the use of **shape memory alloys** (smart wire) to achieve movement.

All of these systems can be used to create dynamic displays. They can be interconnected or used together to achieve the outcome you require.

 D&T Routes Control Products, Control of mechanical systems, page 66

Engineering a graphic product

Graphic products can be 'engineered' for special effects that use mechanisms and movements. These may be for novelty effect, e.g. to surprise or amuse, or they may communicate things that are difficult to put across through a simple drawing.

The diagram at the top of the opposite page shows some mechanisms that you might use to create pop-ups in paper. Remember that pop-up and other engineered graphic products need to be constructed very accurately if they are to work.

Many graphic products make use of simple control systems.

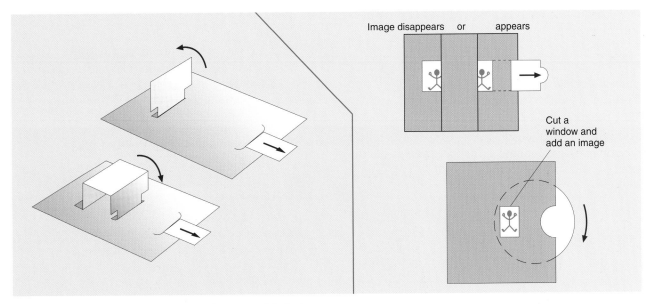

Some mechanisms that you could use (see page 10 also).

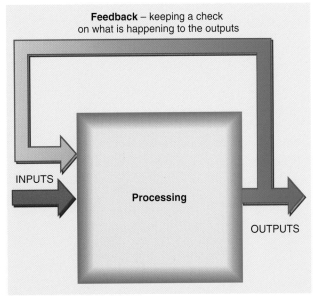

Image disappears   or   appears

Cut a window and add an image

Analysing control systems

What actually happens – the effect that is produced – is known as the **output** of the system. For example: lights flash on and off, a musical tune is played or the display rotates. What causes the effect to happen is the **input**. For example, a sensor or a switch provides an input that switches on the output. All **systems** have inputs and outputs.

The inputs have to be processed to produce the output required. **Input-process-output** diagrams are a very useful way of representing these systems.

Designing mechanical systems into your graphic product

You will find the following helpful when analysing a need and when designing and making a mechanical system to meet it.

I   What do you want to achieve?

Describe the task that the system needs to perform. Describe what you want to achieve as fully as possible using the questions overleaf to help you.

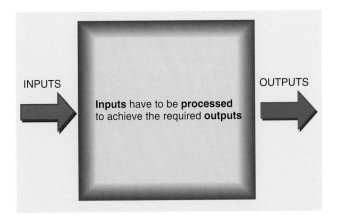

INPUTS

OUTPUTS

Inputs have to be **processed** to achieve the required **outputs**

a) A system contains a **process** that produces **outputs** in response to **inputs**.

Feedback – keeping a check on what is happening to the outputs

INPUTS

Processing

OUTPUTS

b) In **feedback** or **closed-loop** systems information is fed back from the output to the input. This can be used to control the system.

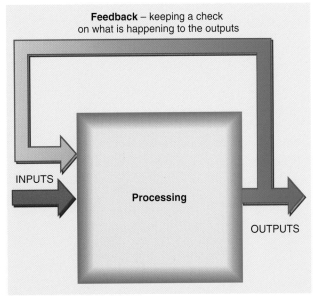

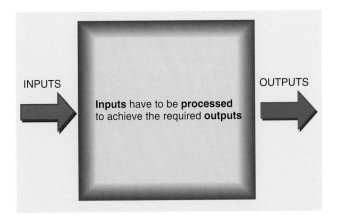

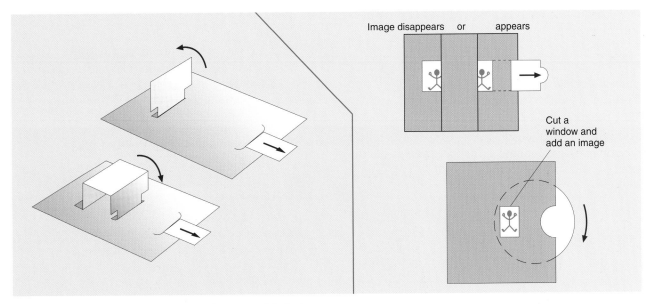

Systems and control

- What do you want to happen? (What **output** do you want?)
- What devices could you use to achieve this?
- What are the advantages and disadvantages of each device?
- What appears to be the best at this stage?

- When and how do you want this output to happen?
- What do you want to cause it to happen?
- Do you want the system to respond to a change or an event?
- How can you detect this change or event?

From	To	Via							Example
		crank/ slider	cams	levers and linkages	gears	rack and pinion/ screw thread	pulleys and belts	gears and chain/ toothed belt	
Rotary	Linear	✓	✓			✓			
Linear	Rotary	✓		✓		✓			
Rotary	Oscillating			✓					
Rotary	Reciprocating	✓	✓						
"x" revolutions per minute (rpm)	"y" revolutions per minute (rpm)				✓		✓	✓	slow / fast
Size X	Size Y			✓					

Types of motion for graphic products

2 Developing some design ideas

Use the information in the table below to work out
which device(s) seems most suitable. Use this to
develop some design ideas.

Mechanical sub-systems

Mechanical sub-system	Type of motion provided	Force or torque (turning force)	Angular movement or distance
Low voltage electric motors (1.5 V or 12 V)	continuous rotary between 4500 and 16 000 rpm with no load – the speed can be controlled electronically • turn through an arc if connected to suitable linkage • linear movement when connected to a crank and slider	available as low, medium and high torque – a gearbox can be used to change output speed or to increase the torque	
Servo motors	partial rotary – turns through an arc	high ~0.25 Nm; various mechanisms can be mounted on the motor to provide different output movements	180° arc
Stepper motors	partial rotary – turns through an arc or complete circle in steps	low ~0.01 Nm	48 (7.5°) or 200 (1.8°) steps per revolution
Linear actuators (6V)	linear at a speed of about 10 mm per second 0.5 mm per revolution of shaft	15–25 N	~40–50 mm
Solenoids: • 12 V miniature • 12 V standard • 12 V large	linear or linear reciprocating Note: when solenoids are 'operated' they draw a continuous electric current	0.5 N at 4 mm 3.5 N at 6 mm 6.0 N at 6 mm	max ~12 mm max ~18 mm max ~18 mm
Pneumatic pistons designed for use in schools	linear or linear reciprocating	up to 100 N	up to 200 mm
Pneumatic air muscles – these are like a balloon in a long, thin net bag; when you pump air into the balloon it pulls the ends of the bag together	linear	~10 N	~50 mm
Hydraulic pistons: • using water filled syringes • using hydraulic kit	linear or linear reciprocating	about 10 N up to 1000 N	up to 100 mm up to 200 mm
'Smart wire' which contracts when you pass a small electric current through it; it expands again when the current is switched off	linear	up to 10 N	a few mm

Notes: Levers and linkages can be combined with solenoids and with pneumatic and hydraulic pistons.
Electronic control be used with all of these devices.

Systems and control

3 Modelling your ideas

You can model your ideas in a number of ways.

◆ Using card to model linkages and cams. This is very useful when a 'trial and error' approach is needed to sort out the dimensions. Use templates to make the components quickly.
◆ Using thin sheets of resistant materials, plywood, acrylic sheet etc. This can be useful once you have sorted out the basic ideas using card, and templates may be useful.
◆ Mechanical systems are available in kits. These kits are a very useful tool in modelling and further developing your design ideas. You can also use them for rapid prototyping of design proposals.

Kits can be used to save time and also enable you to use a wider range of components than you might normally have access to. Also, many of these kits can be interconnected. For example, you can use electronic control with pneumatic or mechanical systems. In this way you can try out and modify complex ideas quickly.

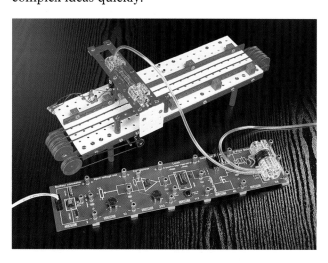

Animating control systems

Control systems can be quite difficult to understand – producing an animation of all or part of a control system can help overcome this problem.

Control systems can be:

◆ mechanical – levers, cams, cranks, gears
◆ pneumatic – using pistons and valves operated by compressed air
◆ electronic
◆ electro-mechanical – using electric motors, solenoids, linear actuators (ramrods), relay switches.

These different types of control system can be interconnected, for example:

◆ electronic control can be used with mechanical, electro-mechanical and pneumatics systems
◆ mechanical systems are often attached to pneumatic pistons.

There are two types of control that are frequently used:

◆ closed-loop or feedback control
◆ sequential control.

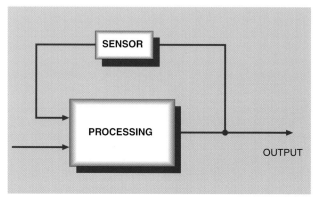

In **feedback control** a sensor is used to keep a check on the output. The sensor feeds back information into the system to keep the output at the required level.

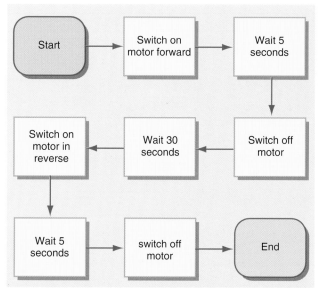

In **sequential control** a series of actions takes place, one after the other, in the correct sequence.

Focused task: *Animating control systems*

Produce an animation to help explain one or both of the two types of control: feedback or sequential. This could be:

■ a working model using diagrams and pictures on pieces of card
■ a computer simulation
■ a series of diagrams or photographs with captions (storyboard)
■ a cartoon strip.

D&T Routes Control Products, Control systems, page 36

Stop and think

When you have completed this task, think about other applications besides graphic products that might use a control system. For example when manufacturing high volumes of products how might systems help with:

● the safety of people who work in a factory?
● controlling the machines that they use?

Control systems in a factory, Southernprint case study, page 83

Case study: *Kipper's Bear – Where, oh where, is Kipper's Bear?*

Kipper's Bear is an interactive pop-up story book by Nick Inkpen. It is aimed at children between the ages 2 and 9 years of age. It is a short story about Kipper, a dog, who has lost his teddy bear. The story follows Kipper as he looks for his teddy, asking his friends, who range from mice and pigs to the pinky-purple bleeper people living on the moon!

Alas no one has seen his bear. Kipper gives up and goes to bed without his bear, not realising that the bear is hiding under the bedclothes reading a book by torch light!

A child can participate in this story by pushing, pulling and opening flaps to reveal or animate different aspects of the story.

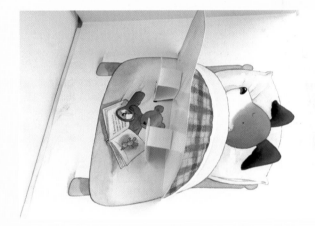

The lifting of the bedclothes operates Kipper's Bear's torch.

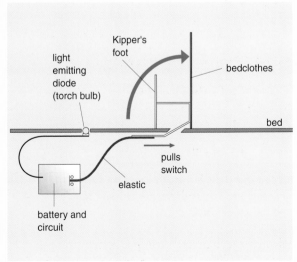

Stop and think

- In the Kipper's Bear example what is the output?
- What is the input?
- How suitable, in your view, is input and output in this case?
- What kinds of materials and construction have been used here?
- Why are they suited to use by young children?

Using electronics

Only a simple lighting effect has been incorporated into the Kipper's Bear pop-up story. You could develop more complex products using an integrated circuit (IC) chip – such as the 555 timer. This can be used:

◆ to make LEDs (**light-emitting diodes** or small 'lights') flash on and off
◆ to produce a sound effect
◆ with sensors to achieve some feedback control.

In other words, to make the lights or sound come on in response to a particular input, such as opening a card or touching part of a display.

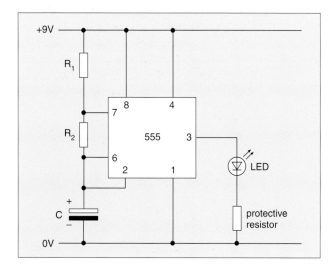

Using a 555 timer IC to produce bursts of light. You can change the ON and OFF times by changing the values of the resistors R_1 and R_2 and the capacitor C.

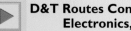

D&T Routes Control Products, Electronics, page 48

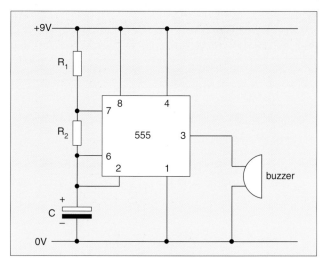

Using a 555 timer IC to produce sounds.

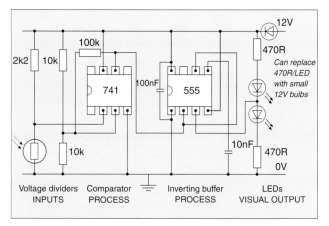

Circuit diagram and PCB layout for the 555 IC used with sensors.

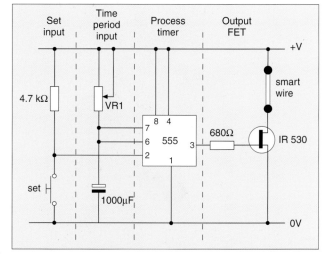

Circuit diagram showing the 555 IC used with smart wire to produce movement.

Case study: *Using electronics in graphic products*

A group of students wanted to produce a colourful display in their school entrance hall as part of some work they were doing on 'Saving the rain forests'. The display would give some idea of the vast range of plants and animals that live in rain forests (biodiversity). While they were working on this they realised that it would be displayed when children from local primary schools and their parents would be visiting, to help them choose which school the children would attend. They decided that an even more exciting interactive display was needed: an *electronic* rain forest!

They achieved the desired effect by using sensors so that as people walked up to and past the display, the bushes rustled as if animals were moving around and the sounds of animals came from loudspeakers. At one point a monkey appeared and rapidly disappeared behind a tree.

Case study: *Cornucopia and the Willowstone greeting card*

Willowstone Ltd manufacture garden pots. The company exhibits its products each year at a trade fair but needs to encourage potential customers by direct mailing to visit their stand. **Cornucopia Ltd** designed and manufactured an unusual, eye-catching product which house-holders would be more likely to read.

'For each of the last five years we have had to devise a new solution which is attractive, informative and long-lasting. We know from experience that this can be achieved by producing a design that involves the use of more than one of the senses – even an interestingly-textured paper can make the recipient hold on to it for a bit longer,' said Lesley Fenton at Cornucopia.

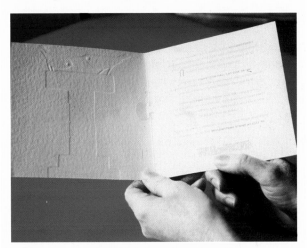

Cornucopia designed and manufactured this embossed card with an image of a Willowstone bird-bath. When opened the bird tweets loudly with the help of a miniature sound module which is concealed in the card.

Values issues

It seems that new and unusual devices are constantly developed, simply to catch our attention or persuade us to buy more products.

◆ How can manufacturers afford to produce complex devices, such as miniature electronic circuits, to be given away free in promotions?
◆ Is it right to include such items in throw-away or novelty items that may only be used once before they are discarded?

79

Manufacturing in higher volumes

Manufacturers often want to produce high volumes of identical graphic products. These can exist in many different forms but most commonly they are manufactured by the printing and publishing industries. In these industries, the impact of IT, together with a long history of using mechanised processes, has placed an emphasis on producing many items quickly and at low unit cost.

> ▶ **D&T Routes Core Book,**
> **Methods of production, page 120**

Printing

Rather than just producing one image, though it is sometimes used for that, printing is about repeating an image over and over from one master image. It was one of the earliest forms of mass-production. Traditionally this was done using blocks or plates. Now photographic methods, as well as computer-stored information, are also commonly used.

People have always wanted to make images and keep them. Cave paintings, patterns carved in wood and bone, ancient Egyptian hieroglyphics carved in stone, illuminated scripts on parchment are all examples. The desire for repeated copies led to a carved technique where ink was added to the surface and pressed onto paper. This method, called **relief printing**, was originally developed by carving away the background in wood but is now mostly carried out using metal.

The patterns on these old wooden printing blocks were cut in relief. Their inked surfaces were pressed onto paper to make the print.

The number of printed copies made is limited to how long the plate, block or stamp will last. There are many different methods of relief printing.

Focused task: Making blocks for relief printing

You can experiment with relief-printing techniques to further develop your understanding of printing methods. Try making a block from a potato to make simple repeat shapes. String and card are also simple to use and can provide quite complex print designs.

Relief printing methods are easy to use in school.

Carry out a brief set of trials using these techniques and retain a sample of each method to include in your portfolio. Write a brief evaluation of your work, including answers to the following questions.

- Which method is easiest?
- Which method gives the clearest printed image?
- What could you do to make them clearer?
- Is each print identical? If not, why is this so? How might you change the process so you get the same impression each time?
- Which block do you think would wear out first? Give reasons for this answer.
- What special properties do you think an industrial printing block, to be used for a print-run of thousands of copies, would need to have?

80

Screen printing

Screen printing is a widely used process. A fine cloth (silk or fine weave synthetic) is stretched tight across a rectangular frame and ink is squeezed through it. Some form of mask (or stencil), blocking out the mesh of the screen, is used to create the image to be printed. It is a very useful method as it allows you to print on many kinds of surface, including metal, plastic, board and fabric. It is the most common process used for labels printed directly onto products. The screen can also be used to print onto non-flat surfaces because of its ability to 'give'.

This silk-screen has been made in school to print onto a T-shirt.

Screen stencils can be made in many ways, including hand or CNC machine-cut film, paper and painted-on liquid. Photographic methods, using light-sensitive emulsion and a light-box, are also commonly used and provide very fine detail. Normally a separate stencil is needed for each different colour in the final design. Screen printing is not suitable for very large print runs as it is slow and labour intensive.

D&T Routes Textiles, page 74

Mass production and high volume printing

When very large numbers of printed products are required, such as high circulation magazines, manufacturers usually use special processes such as **gravure** and **lithography**.

Gravure is an **intaglio** process which means that printing ink is held on the printing plates in grooves rather than on their surface (as in relief printing). It can produce large numbers of very high quality prints, such as postage stamps, fine art prints and photographs.

The grooves are etched into copper plates or solid steel cylinders using acid and when inked, these press the image onto the paper or card at very high speed. The deeper the indentations, which are also known as **cells**, the more ink they can hold. The amount of ink in each cell controls the density of the colour that results. The thin, spirit-based ink is printed on dry paper and dries quickly by evaporation.

Gravure gives excellent quality results and is very good for long runs of 300 000 or more. Printing may take place at speeds up to 50 000 impressions per hour. Setting-up costs (the total cost of getting plates and machines ready) are high but new materials and engraving methods, including by laser, are now improving efficiency and reducing costs in the plate-making process.

See if you can identify these features (e.g. high setting-up costs) on the Volumes of production chart on page 120 of the *D&T Routes Core Book*.

Superior Creative Services case study, page 90

Lithography, or **litho** as it is commonly known, involves no etching or engraving. Instead, the surface of the plate is treated chemically to accept printing ink only in those places where the image is needed and to accept water where it is not needed. The process relies on the fact that water and grease do not mix, to restrict the spread of ink.

After any form of printing the sheets need time for ink and moisture to dry out.

D&T Routes Core Book,
How this book was manufactured,
page 138

Litho plates accept ink only in those places where the image is needed.

Early lithography used smooth stone slabs on a flat press but now thin metal plates are used which can be wrapped around the cylinder of a rotary press. The invention of **offset litho** in the early 1900s came when the images were transferred, or offset, onto a rubber blanket before coming into contact with the paper. These two changes speeded up and refined the process to make it the most common commercial printing method used today.

Offset litho is used for shorter print runs than gravure, usually for batches of no less than 1000, and at speeds between 4000 and 12 000 impressions per hour.

Both gravure and offset litho can be **sheet-fed** or **web-fed** (with ready-cut papers or continuously fed from a roll).

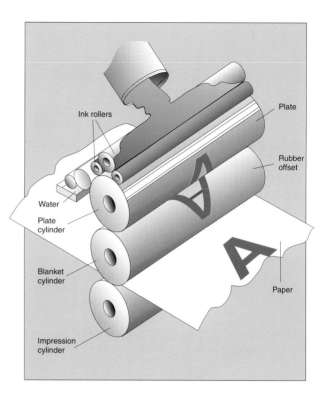

The rubber offset, shown in this diagram, improved the litho process and helped reduce wear on the delicate printing plate.

Printing photographs with gravure and offset litho

Only a limited number of different coloured inks are used on any one print so the different tones (lighter and darker variations of a colour) needed when printing a photograph are achieved by breaking the image down into varying sizes of dots. These are produced on a **halftone screen**.

A special screen creates the effect of tones using dots of varying sizes.

Colour pictures are built up from combinations of four different plates: black, cyan, magenta, and yellow. The same principles that you will have learned in science and art, where mixing primary colours can create any other colour in the spectrum, apply here. Black is also added for contrast and shadows.

Each colour image has to be scanned with special screens to filter out its different process colours. These halftone screens are applied at different angles and when their colours are printed on top of each other they create a 'rosette' effect which can only be seen under a magnifying glass. To the naked eye the overlapping coloured dots blur to provide a realistic colour.

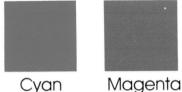 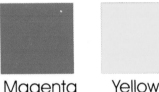

Cyan   Magenta   Yellow

Cyan, magenta and yellow process colours.

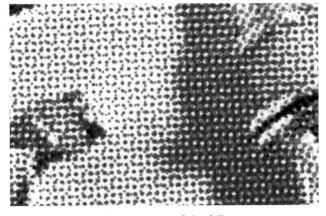

Here you can see the creation of the full colour image and the 'rosette' effect.

Stop and think

Easy availability of printed products means we can take for granted the high levels of skill needed for their production. By examining printed products more carefully you can find clues to some of the processes used to manufacture them. Visiting a print shop would help a lot.

Keep an eye out for bad printing. You may see a **moiré** effect, or blurring, when the plates are not **registered** properly and some bad prints have slipped through the **quality control procedures** at the printing works.

Sometimes you can see the printer's **colour boxes,** or colour identification marks and the registration marks through which they check that the different screens have lined up exactly. Look for them inside the joins of disassembled cereal boxes.

Case study: *Southernprint (Web Offset) Ltd*

Dorset-based Southernprint prints magazines, brochures and catalogues for some of the UK's top publishing houses. It uses five web offset heatset presses which can each produce up to 40 000 copies per hour in full colour.

Paper is supplied in large reels (each containing up to 15 kilometres of paper) and each press uses one reel every 30–40 minutes. Reels are spliced (joined) at the full press speed and, in the event of a web break (i.e. a break in the paper), the press is automatically brought to a halt.

The printed web is dried in gas ovens which ensure that the ink does not smudge or mark when it goes through the folder at the end of the press.

Sophisticated computer controls are used at every stage in the process to ensure proper print register and the highest quality throughout.

D&T Routes Core Book, Control in Automated Manufacture, page 150

MANUFACTURING

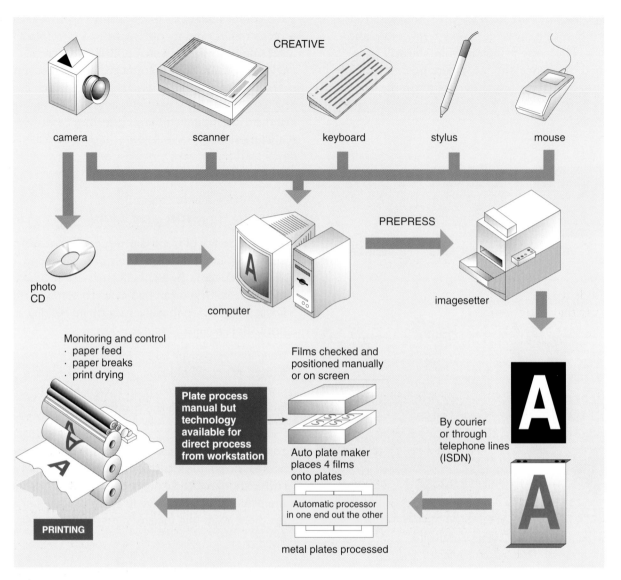

From design to print

Focused task: *Printing processes*

Based on the information you have read in this section, which method(s) do you think would be best for:

- long runs of production?
- short runs?
- batch production of 200?
- full colour?

Write an account, giving reasons for your choices and including reference to such things as setting-up costs (making the plates and setting the printing machinery), unit costs (the cost of an individual printed item) and speed (the number of impressions per hour).

Stop and think

The invention of printing has greatly influenced our lives.

How often do we encounter words and images created by the printing and publishing industries?

Record how many times in a day you see or use print. Include such things as reading papers and magazines, as well as walking past advertisements on shops and buses on the way to and from school.

Values issues

◆ How different would our world be without printed images?
◆ How can industry afford to manufacture complex printed objects, often requiring advanced technology, which are frequently casually discarded by the public?

Binding

Binding is the process whereby a set of sheets of paper are fixed together to make them into a single document. An ordinary bent-wire paper clip is a very simple, temporary, binding method. Books and products containing many pages need appropriate methods to make them handle, appear and last in the way that customers expect.

You can use simple binding methods in school. But careful choice and planning is needed to get a good quality result.

Ties and punched holes make interesting binding methods.

Spiral and plastic comb binding

Plastic or metal spines are fixed by a simple machine into a continuous row of pre-punched holes. This is used where you want your pages to lie flat, say for photocopying.

Staples and saddle-stitching

You can use a staple machine to insert staples into the centre, or **spine**, of a thin document. A jig

arrangement, or simple marked **register**, is needed to position these staples accurately. Commercially manufactured products use special stapling or **saddle-stitching**, so called because the pages are sewn together with wires while they are held securely over a metal 'saddle'. The complete magazine goes under a head that puts in wire staples cut from a coil. This method is limited to fairly thin items with few pages.

Perfect binding

This simple, low-cost method is often used on thick magazines and paperback books. The sections are pre-trimmed and glue is spread down the spine before the cover is glued on. A draw-back of this method is that the spine may split, allowing pages to fall out, if the product is pressed flat or when it is well used.

Sewn binding

The covers and pages of hard-back books are usually sewn together. Threads are sewn into each section (or signature) and more threads are used to hold all the sections together. New methods use additional plastic threads to reduce costs, increase speed of production and improve durability.

The key points when binding are to be very precise when trimming and to allow space at the binding edge so that the page layout is not interfered with.

For more information about printing methods ask your teacher for a worksheet that explains them in greater detail.

Tolerances, templates and quality

In an ideal world manufactured products would be absolutely identical as well as exactly the size the designer specified. In practice most batch- or mass-produced objects are slightly different due to gradual wear in machines or human error. This will usually be acceptable because the designer will have included **tolerances** within the design. This means working to an upper and lower limit between which an object will be of an acceptable size to function correctly.

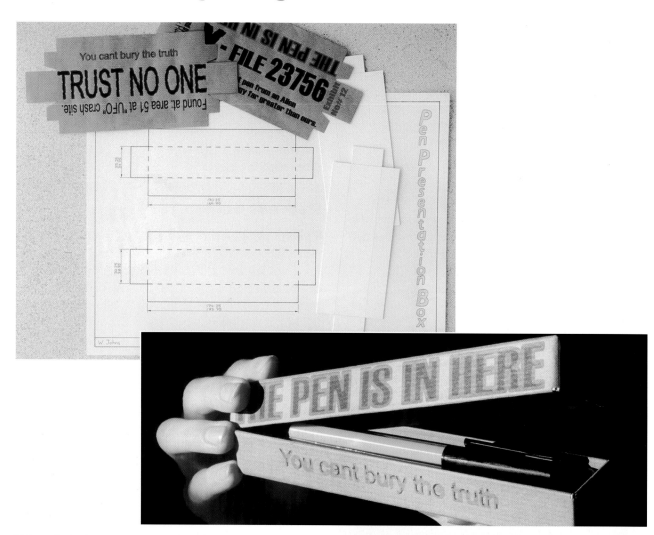

When designing a pen presentation box, some students found that no more than 0.5 mm variation (±0.25 mm tolerance) could be allowed in the construction, to avoid the lid feeling too loose or too tight.

Sampling and quality control

Using quality control checks, manufacturers will take samples of a product at regular intervals during production. Each is checked to make sure that the products stay within the specified tolerance limits. Samples that go outside specified **tolerance limits** will not be used and the production process will be modified to achieve **zero defects**. This will reduce wastage and cost for the manufacturer.

Quality control will be part of a manufacturer's overall approach to quality assurance.

This student is using a card template to check that cutting was accurate when batch-producing pen presentation boxes. This quality control method will help avoid time-consuming mistakes later.

D&T Routes Core Book, Quality and evaluation, page 153

Manufacturing with press knives

Press knives are the main tools used to cut repeat shapes from sheets of card in the printing and packaging industries. The knife, or shaped cutter, is used to press out the required shapes from sheets of material just like gingerbread men with a pastry cutter. Very complex shapes can result including both cropping around an outline and perforating for folds.

Each press knife is a **cutting die** consisting of a backplate, knife-thin strips of metal outlining the shape to be cut and a synthetic sponge on each side.

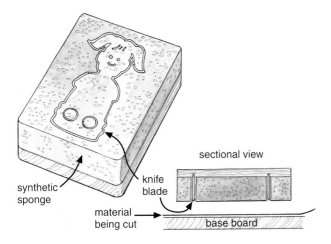

synthetic sponge

knife blade

sectional view

material being cut → base board

The press knife principle

The knife is placed in a press and forced down through many sheets of card to cut out a number to the required shape. The synthetic foam ensures the card is pushed away from the cutter and does not stick in the press knife when the press is raised.

Two finger puppets and their press knife cutters.

A large back-plate can hold a number of different outlines allowing a range of parts to be cut at the same time from a sheet of card. This is useful when cutting shapes for pop-up cards and books. The knife-thin strips of metal can be given a variety of edges to achieve different types of cut.

Case study: The Cornucopia envelope

Cornucopia is a small graphics and exhibition design company. Its clients range from small manufacturing businesses to local authorities and large multi-national technology companies. The company design and produce brochures, leaflets, promotional material, corporate identities, stationery and exhibition graphics.

Press knives are ideal for products that need fine tolerances, including card shapes and mechanisms.

▶ **Willowstone case study, page 79**

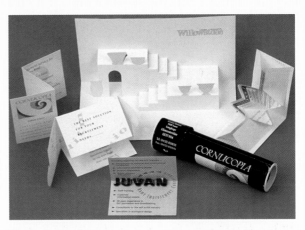

These promotional products are manufactured with the aid of press knives.

Focused task: Press knife products

Find some products, such as those with complex outline-cuts and perforated folds, that you think have been made with press knives.

Describe, using sketches and notes, the different kinds of product you have found.

How important are tolerances to the function of each product?

CAD/CAM

The use of **computer-aided design** and **computer-aided manufacture** by industry has increased dramatically over the last few years. It has provided manufacturers with a number of advantages, including time-savings, reduction of waste, more standardised production and increased reliability.

> ▶ **D&T Routes Core Book,**
> **Using computers for manufacture,**
> **page 132**

Cutting and engraving images

A variety of CAD/CAM equipment may be available to you in school. Besides printers, you may have a plotter, plotter-cutter, engraver, sewing machine or CNC milling machine, each of which can manufacture a product directly from a CAD file.

The plotter-cutter

A plotter-cutter is a variation on the *x-y* plotter. It cuts the lines in a CAD file instead of drawing them with a pen. It is useful for cutting out shapes from sheet materials such as thin card and self-adhesive vinyl. A common application is the production of signs for the sides of vehicles. Vinyl **vehicle graphics** have many advantages over traditional hand-painting including their speed of application, accuracy and the fact that they can be easily removed if the vehicle is sold at a later date.

This tiny blade is mounted on a pen shaft and is able to cut very accurately on the lines in a CAD file.

The same technique can be used to apply graphics to a wide range of products designed and made in school.

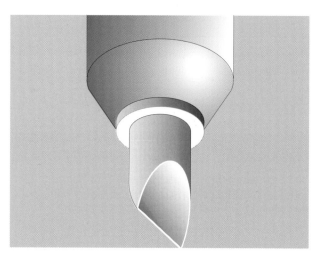

Some students' use of cut vinyl graphics

Unlike with press knives, when using a plotter-cutter shapes can be easily varied by altering the CAD file. Very large shapes can also be cut by feeding material from a roll under the cutter.

The main advantages of using this method include:

◆ accuracy
◆ **re-scaling**, or accurately re-creating the design larger or smaller
◆ repeatability.

It is important to be able to think in layers of colour. Sometimes it is better to apply the cut-out shapes such as text, at other times it is better to remove the top layer and show the layer below. This is especially useful when you want fairly small text such as on the NatWest folders above. To create this effect the text was removed from the black vinyl and the white vinyl underlayer allowed to show through. This technique can be used in various different ways.

The same technique was used by students to produce the graphics on these mugs. Glaze was painted onto the mugs using plotter cut stencils. The stencils burned off in the kiln when the mug was fired.

A similar technique can be used to produce a silk-screen printing stencil. When using a plotter-cutter to produce a stencil the image simply needs reversing prior to plotting.

Shapes can also be cut from scanned images, as well as from lines in a CAD file.

Screen printing, page 81

This machine can cut small shapes that it has previously scanned.

Engraving an image with CAD/CAM

Lines cut into the surface, but not completely through the material, may be called **engraving**. The pattern on the drinks coasters below was produced using a computer-controlled engraving machine. Scanned images may also be engraved. Engraving into special layered materials means that coloured lines can be exposed underneath as the top layer is cut away. This technique is often used for graphics on electrical control gear and industrial machinery as it is very durable.

Embroidering an image

CAD/CAM can provide a stitched or embroidered output provided machinery is available. Embroidered logos, such as those seen on uniforms and worn as part of a corporate identity, are often manufactured in this way.

A badge being embroidered on a computer-controlled embroidery machine.

There is more to a company than a product and a production line. Somebody has to organise the company, employ and train staff, pay wages, process orders, find buyers, arrange deliveries, and so on. It is not enough for a company to manufacture a good product. Managing the different parts of a business properly means getting the **right quantity** of the **right product** to the **right place** at the **right time** to sell at the **right price**.

Who are the manufacturers?

Different kinds of manufacturing are located in every region of the United Kingdom.

The sector of manufacturing that uses paper, printing and publishing is the largest single group, although the combined engineering and allied industries are greater when taken as a whole. The case study which follows is to help you understand the variety of work that takes place within a manufacturing company. You might compare it with case studies from other sectors of manufacturing contained in the other *D&T Routes* books to develop a broader picture.

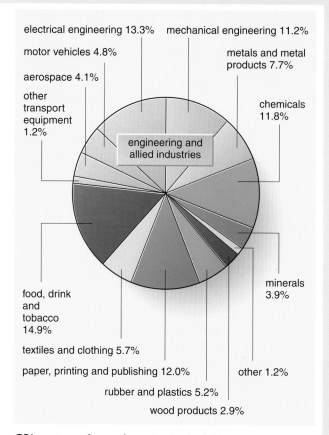

electrical engineering 13.3%
mechanical engineering 11.2%
motor vehicles 4.8%
metals and metal products 7.7%
aerospace 4.1%
other transport equipment 1.2%
chemicals 11.8%
engineering and allied industries
minerals 3.9%
food, drink and tobacco 14.9%
textiles and clothing 5.7%
other 1.2%
paper, printing and publishing 12.0%
rubber and plastics 5.2%
wood products 2.9%

CBI sectors of manufacturing in the UK.

Case study: Superior Creative Services Ltd

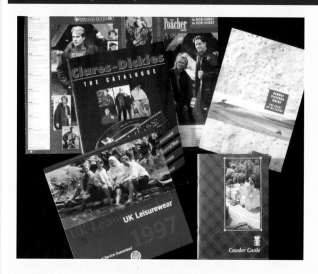

Superior Creative Services Ltd produces a range of printed materials such as catalogues, sales brochures, company reports, headed note-paper and advertisements for newspapers. They design and print these in-house, carrying out all the processes involved from first ideas through to finished product. They handle the publications for some of Britain's best known businesses, including Marks and Spencer.

Superior Creative Services is a medium-size company which has been operating since 1976. It can be found in Melksham, Wiltshire, not far from the M4 motorway. This gives it good access to the motorway network.

Working with clients

The company prides itself on the way it works with its clients. It responds directly to their needs and works closely with them to ensure client satisfaction.

Clients can talk frequently to the company using video conferencing, so avoiding the need to travel long distances to meetings. This means that work in progress can be checked and agreed quickly.

One of the most important aspects of a job is establishing the initial brief with the client, finding out what the client wants, and working out how this can be achieved. Rather than use sales staff, the director (a designer) will meet with the client and work through initial ideas. Once agreed, the director can work out how much it will cost and give a clear brief on the project to the design team.

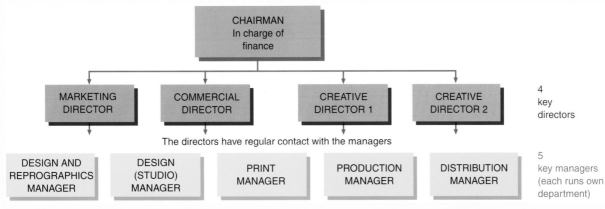

The directors have regular contact with the managers

4 key directors

5 key managers (each runs own department)

Running the company

The Managing Director, who has overall responsibility for the running of the company, is in constant touch with the four key directors who control the company's operations. They guide and oversee the work of the different departments in the Melksham plant which are run by five managers (see diagram). Each department contains operatives with a range of skills.

Computers are used to manage design and production in the company. The **Optimus Management System** (**OMS**) carries all the information about a particular job (client's requirements, type of paper, number to be produced etc.) along with an estimate of costs for each stage of production. After a brief has been agreed with a client, the details of the job are fed into the system and given a job number. The materials and hours it will take are estimated and the costs involved calculated automatically. If the client wants more work done, this can be added to the job details and OMS will provide revised costs.

This means that, using the computer network in the plant, any manager can see exactly how long each part of a job is taking and whether it is sticking to the estimated time and costs. Not only can the management keep track of a job but they can also keep the costs under review, an important part of business management.

Producing a catalogue

What are the stages involved in producing any type of printed product? We can look at these by following a sales catalogue through the production process.

 D&T Routes Core Book, How this book was manufactured, page 138

Stage 1 Meeting with clients

A meeting is arranged with the client to work out a brief for the job. An estimate of the work and costs involved, based on the number of pages, is worked out.

Stage 2 Concept work

Developing the product concept.

Some concept work is done in the design studio. This might involve drawing up initial layouts and placing photographs (from the company's photo-library) in position. This is just to see what the pages will look like. The real photographs will be put in later. This is presented to the client along with the estimates of cost.

Stage 3 Copy and photographs

The client sends the copy (the words) to go in the catalogue or may ask Superior Creative Services to write the copy based on information it provides. The copy is put into a text file on the computer. Any photographs will be **art-directed** and **shot**.

Stage 4 Layouts

The photographs are scanned into a Macintosh computer in a special section of the studio and then sent across to the designer. The designer accesses the text files and photograph files while working on the page layouts. When these have been completed they are sent to the client for checking. These are called **proofs**. At this stage they will be just laser-print copies not final quality prints.

Stage 5 Colour proofs

After any changes required by the client have been made, the layouts go into a more complex tectronic proofing system. This produces high-resolution colour proofs, or prototypes of the pages showing the exact colours intended. These allow for minor changes to be made and will also be used later to check the colours of the copies coming off the printing machine.

Stage 6 Making the plates

Litho printing plates are made using a photographic method.

The computer files are now put onto to special **film** which is used to make the printing plates using an **electro-photographic** process. The film negatives are placed on an unexposed plate which is then exposed to ultra-violet light to create the images.

 Litho printing, page 82

Stage 7 Printing

The plates are put onto the printing machine. When colour is being printed, four plates per page are used to put the colours on in layers. Four primary colours, layered on in different combinations, make up the whole colour spectrum.

The offset litho printing machine has four sections, each section putting on a colour as the page goes through. Sometimes a fifth roller is used to **emboss**, or texture, the surface of the product to give an appropriate 'feel'.

The printed pages are then taken to a different part of the plant where they are **collated** (sorted into order), folded and stitched. They are then packed in boxes ready for delivery.

Production planning

The whole printing operation is handled by the production planning department. The printing machines run for 24 hours a day. They are extremely expensive pieces of equipment and have to run continually to earn their money. This means that the production department have to plan all the jobs well in advance and make sure that people in the printing department know exactly what they have to do. Work is scheduled up to seven weeks in advance at any given time. The Production Team Manager has to monitor this whole operation and make sure that the machines are kept running.

In the design studio

The design studio is at the centre of Superior Creative Services. The company will be judged on the quality of its design and its creative work. But it is not only designers who work here. There are a range of jobs requiring different skills.

Designers

There are two main types of designers in the studio:

1 Senior designers

They make the creative decisions. It is their job to give a brief some 'design magic' to make it special. They do the main page layouts, setting out the position and size of images and text. Much of this is done on the Macintosh computer but often the designers work out their initial ideas on paper on drawing boards. The company values traditional drawing skills and understanding of line and form, as some of the key elements of good design. The senior designers will often present their work to clients.

2 Junior designers

They work to the instructions of the senior designers. They take the page-layout design and make the images and text fit. Sometimes the same basic design is applied to several pages and the junior designer has to make quite a lot of decisions about how to fit everything within the design framework. Junior designers also work on more straightforward jobs like designing an advert for a newspaper.

Reading proofs and handling copy

It is very important that there are no mistakes in copy of any publication whether it is a 40 page company report or a half-page advert. So there are proof-readers in the studio to check for spelling and punctuation mistakes as

well as grammatical errors. Some of the readers also type in copy to save the designer's time. They arrange the word-processor copy in a **text file** so that it is easy for the designers to import it into their page layout.

Handling photographs

Most publications today use photographic images. The first stage is to scan the photograph into the computer. Then the photographs have to be changed to fit the page layout. This might mean they have to be made smaller or larger or they have to be **cropped**, because only part of the photograph is required. Sometimes a designer only wants a **cut-out**, e.g. a person or a product cut out of the background. All these processes are carried out by skilled people in a special part of the studio.

Making the films

The last main process before the printing plates are made is film-making. The page layouts are taken and put onto film. They are arranged so that the pages can be printed in the right order (**imposition**). Also, separate films have to be made for the four different colours used in the printing process.

Making it all fit together

We can look at an example of how the process works for a full-page advert for a magazine.

1   The senior designer gets a **brief** setting out what the client wants. He or she draws up a **page layout** on paper, or on screen, showing how the advert will work and the space given to pictures and text.

2   This is handed on to the junior designers to do. They have to take the guides for the layout and make it all fit exactly.

3   The copy is typed in and given to the designer in a **text file**. The photographs are scanned into the computer and sized or cropped according to the instructions from the designer. A **photo file** is created.

4   The junior designer places photographs and text on a page layout on the computer screen. The results are printed on a laser copy and the proof-reader checks that there are no mistakes.

5   The results are shown to the designer in charge and the client for their approval. If there are no changes to be made, the disk containing the page layout is given to the **film maker** who turns it into film ready for the printing department.

Index

TEACHER'S NOTES

INTRODUCTION
Using the D&T Routes Focus Area Books

This book, produced by the Royal College of Art Schools Technology Project, is one of a suite of five focus area books: *Resistant Materials*; *Food*; *Control Products*; *Textiles* and *Graphic Products*. Each has a teacher's version like this with 16 extra pages.

Each of the books has a similar structure and they are designed to be used together with the *D&T Routes Core Book*. This provides students with a D&T study guide as well as information and tasks to develop skills in and understanding of: analysing and evaluating products; designing and manufacturing. The focus area books extend items covered in the *Core Book* and contain information and activities that are exclusive to their focus.

Each focus area book contains the following components:

◆ Three full **designing and making assignments** (DMAs) comprising a **Challenge** for students together with supporting focused tasks and case studies
◆ Five or six outline DMAs which present students with a design and make challenge and some starting points to help them get going
◆ **Designing** and **Manufacturing** sections containing focused tasks, information and case studies to support students' designing and making in the focus area
◆ A section on **The Business of Manufacturing** providing further material on manufacturing industry, essential for students following a GNVQ Manufacturing course. It will also enhance GCSE D&T students' understanding of industrial designing and manufacturing.

Using the DMAs on a GCSE D&T course

The full DMAs could be treated as a set of 'focused' assignments to provide a Y10 course that will equip students with the skills and understanding to tackle a more extended assignment in Y11. The outline DMAs provide students with ideas that they can use directly or scope for individual interpretation.

Alternatively:

◆ the outline DMAs could be worked up and used in Y10
◆ a student could use one of the full DMAs as their main coursework assignment in Y11
◆ teachers can use the DMAs in the book as models to develop their own assignments or to modify existing successful ones.

The Designing and Manufacturing sections can be used to support DMAs taken from the book or any assignment developed by either students or teachers.

Using the focus area books to support work in other materials

Although each book can be used without reference to the other focus area books, they are written so that each provides a useful resource to support the others. Two examples: information and activities in the *Control Products* book can be used to support work on systems and control in the other focus areas; and one DMA – **Survival**, appears in all of the focus area books. Also many DMAs in the books provide contexts for the design and manufacture of products in a range of materials.

Using the books to support GNVQ Manufacturing

The books are designed for use with Full or Part 1 programmes leading to Foundation and Intermediate awards. Using the complete set of focus area books with your students will allow you to support their needs across the different manufacturing sectors.

The Business of Manufacturing section provides material that meets the requirements of GNVQ Manufacturing linked to the particular focus area or manufacturing sector. The DMAs and the Designing and Manufacturing sections provide a range of assignments and tasks that can be used to meet the Evidence Indicators.

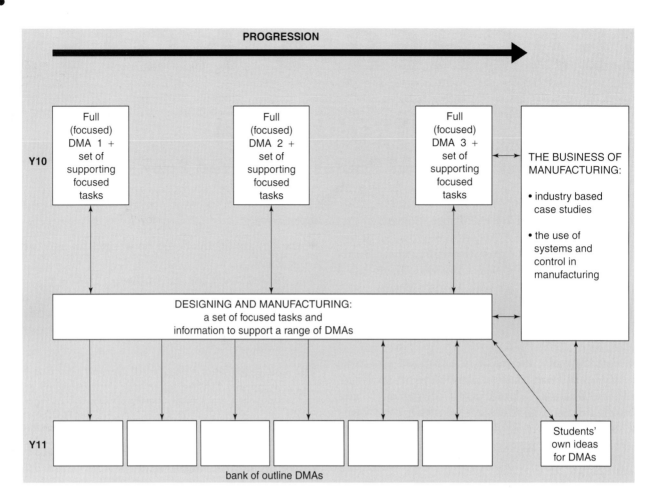

A model for using the DMAs to provide a KS4 course.

A summary of the DMAs in the Graphic Products book

DMA Designing & Making Context	Special Features	Learning Outcomes	References to D & T Routes Core Book
Survival Products which help people in testing situations	Open-ended task for use in any focus area (link two?). Focuses on special needs in special situations so requires analysis of context and user needs Outcome at any level of complexity – good differentiation possible	**All must:** produce a product which helps identified people in a specific situation **Most should:** have researched the situation thoroughly and produced a relevant response **Some could:** produce a set of products relevant to different needs in the situation	Clarifying intentions 48 Initial ideas 53 Thinking about function 66 Using your research 90–95 Testing 113 Planning your manufacture 126
Pop-ups Card construction task with plenty of opportunity for creativity	Balanced appeal across genders, design-for-need focus as it stresses a 'useful' product. Individuals could emphasise creative/innovative or clear descriptive approach Illustration skills demanded	**All must:** complete at least a single working pop-up **Most should:** pop-up their own illustration(s) **Some could:** complete a complex product developed from primary research	Briefing yourself 48 Design specifications 51 & 106 See also the D & T Challenges Red Book 105–6 Modelling in card

[Table continues opposite.]

Table continued

DMA Designing & Making Context	Special Features	Learning Outcomes	References to D&T Routes Core Book
Corporate identity Student identifies organisation, range of products	Strong opportunities for research and inter-personal skills in problem-identification. Opportunities for IT work with lettering. Good vehicle for basic graphics skills in a fully demanding design context	**All must:** produce a basic design and apply it to several products. **Most should:** research a real context for themselves **Some could:** produce a full professional range of applications	Using your research 90–95 Thinking about function 66 and aesthetics 68 Communicating designs 108–111
Photostories Storyboard based. Drawing, photography and/or digital images	Teenager-friendly. Good links to work in English, concentrating on a well-structured story analysed into a sequence of images. Opportunities to learn about market niches and target audiences as well as new image technologies	**All must:** plan, and sequence in images, a simple story **Most should:** produce this in photo/digital images **Some could:** exploit digital imaging and image manipulation at a sophisticated level	Making things happen 14 How to manage your time 16 Thinking about aesthetics 68 Communicating designs 108
Packaging Familiar topic – but open-ended.	Appearance and functional considerations in balance. Potential for professional quality product & enhanced industrial understanding	**All must:** identify own purposes **Most should:** complete a high quality product **Some could:** explore complex nets	Generating initial ideas 53–63 Specifications 51, 106 & 147 Product life 88
Constructional play Toys for building from cardboard packages	Real research need. Creative opportunities within tight constraints. Very motivating for many students. Continual testing needed in design development	**All must:** conduct genuine primary research **Most should:** design challenging & fun constructions for children **Some could:** submit designs to companies for production	Using your research 90–95 Kits, card & corny ideas 58 Limitations 59
Getting the picture Graphic statistics display	Good practice in understanding numbers – maths & business studies links. Creative opportunity in a context students are familiar with but have little experience in	**All must:** find their own source numbers **Most should:** produce an original presentation which communicates clearly **Some could:** produce a dynamic display – possibly using IT	Thinking about aesthetics 68–73 Communicating designs 108–111
3D T-Shirts Constructed 3D add-ons to more traditional approaches	Stimulating/unusual. Good values issues opportunity. Collaboration with textiles. Demanding on 3D thinking. Volume production extension opportunities	**All must:** complete a personalised T-shirt **Most should:** exploit the 3D opportunity with originality **Some could:** go into volume production and sell their products	Products & customers 37 Specifications 51 & 106 Generating initial ideas 53–63 Thinking about aesthetics 68–73 Production lines 128–131

A guide to the designing and making assignments (DMAs) in this book

The DMAs in this book have been written with the **graphic design materials** commonly used in schools in mind. The severe limitations of schools' finances are recognised as many graphics materials are too expensive for normal use there. However, insights are given into the commercial world of graphic products and, as is commonly the case, the possibility of individual students sourcing more expensive materials and media, especially for Y11 DMAs is acknowledged.

These Teacher's Notes include some reflection on the nature of a post-1995 Order Graphic Products course and some background information to help you place your course in a contemporary industrial context. Also, a photocopiable glossary is located at the back of this section for use by students.

Graphic Design, Graphic Communication and Graphic Products

You may be developing the Graphic Products course focus with your students from a previous experience of Design and Communication. If so, the revised National Curriculum Design and Technology Order and the changing world of commercial design and industrial manufacturing beyond school now make considerable demands for change on you. The *Graphic Products* concept is quite different as it represents one way for students to achieve their full national curriculum Design and Technology entitlement. That the course is a version of Design and Technology, rather than a free-standing course in its own right, places extra responsibilities on it to ensure that students on the course can develop all aspects of the D&T programme of study in both designing and making. These though do not always coincide with parallels in the adult world of graphic design employment.

If you see an advertisement that just states *Designer* you can be 99% sure that this will be for a *graphic designer*. What does this tell us? Mainly it reflects the fact that the most numerous designers are graphic designers. The reasons for this are various including that:

◆ a lot of graphic design goes on: we produce vast amounts of text/image based information
◆ graphic information needs to be designed well
◆ most people cannot design good graphics (ergo – graphic design is rigorous)
◆ people value well-designed graphics (and criticise poor graphic design readily).

An argument can easily be made, based on these points, to support the inclusion of graphic designing in the curriculum. It can also be supported in terms of its potential value to young people as graphic design requires analytical skills in the handling of information, creative skills in generating appropriate and effective ideas and skills in the generation and selection of images and text. It is also but one small step away from the very powerful influences on them through animated computer games, cartoons and television and cinema advertisements.

The 'designer label' or brand image is another powerful influence on teenagers. How are we to protect children against commercial manipulation without exposing the way it works, in school? What better way of 'unpacking' the components of advertisers' techniques than to give children practical experience of doing it?

The place of graphic design in the curriculum has been dogged by a lack of clarity about its boundaries. Is it art or is it design and technology? Where else is it taught? Very few teachers have the capability to deal successfully with all the demands of a high quality GCSE course in D&T Graphic Products, especially to include the IT dimension adequately. However, many teachers across the curriculum contribute to students' graphics capability.

InSET: Reviewing graphics in the school

This activity is designed for Art and D&T teachers and perhaps, others who teach some graphics, in Media Studies, Biology, in English or Geography.

Resources: Some very varied examples of graphic design, e.g. adverts, newspapers, magazines, Valentine's day card, map, scientific diagram, financial charts (e.g. pie diagrams and histograms), school prospectus, text book, printed t-shirt.

What it means to me

In separate subject groups, pass the items around and quickly note what messages – overt and covert – each item projects to you. Then go round the group asking each member to report what they noted, one item at a time. See how varied the responses are.

Ask each member of the group to state in one sentence why students' graphic skills are important in their lessons.

Coherence and diversity – across the curriculum

Now ask when and in which subject, do students pay special attention to graphics skills? How do the subjects differ in their emphases? Do they use the same key vocabulary? Could these experiences be phased better?

Why D&T Graphic Products?

The emphasis brought in by new GCSE courses since the 1995 revised Order for Design and Technology on, not graphics *per se* but on graphic **products**, draws new boundaries which omit some aspects of graphic design and instead stress others. A place remains in Art in GCSE, GCE and GNVQ courses for graphics work with a different emphasis. Hopefully, schools and colleges will recognise the closeness of these areas and will exploit the expertise of their staff in whichever department.

A key issue as identified in the NC programme of study: (KS4 2a)

'Pupils should be given opportunities to: apply skills, knowledge and understanding from the programmes of study of other subjects, where appropriate, including art, mathematics and science.'

As a sub-set of Design and Technology, the aims of Graphic Products courses are centred on design and technological capability, and students in this area are expected to have no less understanding of the wider issues of D&T than any other. These include understanding the values issues in the relationship of the products to society and commercial manufacturing methods. Graphic Products courses are simply an alternative vehicle through which some students practise and understand Design and Technology as well as students in the other 'focus areas'.

For this reason we find ourselves in something of a tangle with respect to *what is a graphic product* and what is just graphic design. The examination boards will play a significant part in ensuring that these decisions are concluded sensibly. It is this Project's position that a too narrow and pedantic position will undermine the potential value of the subject to its students.

There will remain a place for the practice of 'pure' graphic design without it being always focused on 'products'. Sometimes students' focus will need to be on the component skills, developing their sophistication in the use of visual imagery or in the crisp use of text. This is the purpose of an FPT (focused practical task). By contrast, any Graphic Products designing and making assignment will be expected to have the potential for all aspects of Design and Technology to be experienced, focused on a final product. Our position is that the more closely linked the FPTs and the DMA are, the better, so that the focused tasks enhance students' ability to carry out a DMA better. This approach keeps the main purpose of the course to be students' all-round skills in Design and Technology, despite close attention at times to graphic design, as it may more commonly be known in the adult world.

Art and Graphic Products

Whilst a National Curriculum programme of study is not provided for Art at KS4, it is worth studying the one for KS3 in this context. The aims of Art and D&T clearly coincide totally in the graphics area. Close study suggests that every KS3 Art programme of study statement should be accepted as a guide for D&T Graphic Products teachers.

Sample issues identified in the NC programme of study – for Art, KS3:

3   *In order to develop visual literacy, pupils should be taught about the different ways in which ideas, feelings and meanings are communicated in visual form.*
'Pupils should be given opportunities to:
7c *explore and use two- and three-dimensional media, working on a variety of scales.*
7e *develop understanding of the work of . . . designers, applying knowledge to their own work*

Design and Technology teachers should also study closely the requirements of GCSE Art syllabuses and GNVQ Art and Design specifications to note the considerable overlap with Graphic Products. Many schools and colleges will exploit these through teaching contributions to the D&T course from Art colleagues.

Including commercial/industrial understanding

A key issue as identified in the NC programme of study: (rubric)

*'Pupils should be taught to develop their design and technology capability through combining their **Designing** and **Making** skills . . . with **knowledge and understanding** . . . in order to design and make products.'*

Many graphic products in the commercial world are produced from what GCSE courses call **resistant materials**. There is therefore, a tightrope to be walked by both teacher and student in ensuring that the graphic product the student is involved with is acceptable for assessment. Even the GCSE 'safe' area of packaging is rarely, in industry, concerned with which particular materials are used. Perfume may be packaged in a glass bottle, with labelling embossed into it, capped with metal and enclosed in card. To consider only the card part a 'graphic product', is patently absurd, but a teacher's prior concern must always be to protect their students in the assessment jungle.

However, it is necessary to give students as many insights into and as much practical experience as possible in the commercial/industrial world of graphic product design and manufacture. Whilst understanding can be gained through the case studies in this and the *D&T Routes Core Book* (e.g. page 138), videos, visits and discussion, real experience will only be achieved through designing and making assignments which are industrially relevant.

A key issue as identified in the NC programme of study:

1a *Taken together these assignments should require activity related to industrial practices .*
3c *Pupils should be taught to design for manufacturing in quantity.*

Materials such as paper and board (card) that need simple manufacturing techniques lend themselves well to simulated industrial production in the classroom. The *D&T Routes Core Book* (page 136) shows a textiles exercise that could easily be adapted to a card folder type of product such as a multiple CD holder (see also the *D&T Routes Core Book* page 128). The *D&T Routes Teacher's Resource for KS4* also includes guidance on running industrial simulations (page 118). Sub-sections of products also lend themselves well to a number of students working together to produce a batch. Examples from the DMAs in this book might include standard pop-up mechanisms or mechanical parts for a dynamic display to provide sub-assemblies for individualised full products. You can use the Special Features, Learning Outcomes and Useful References for each, as identified in the chart at the beginning of this section, to help you select what is needed at any point in the course.

Visits to local industry can play a vital part in developing your understanding as well as the students'. One of the advantages of a Graphic Products course is that almost every locality has commercial activity in the field – at the very least, a small jobbing printer and many schools have their own print-shop of some scale. Many teachers have found that undertaking an industrial placement is an extremely valuable means to develop learning materials for students and a worthwhile activity in the summer months.

Properties of materials needed for higher volumes of production

While it is usual for the designer, rather than printer, to select paper with the right look and feel its properties must also be matched to the print process. Paper-based materials vary greatly in structure and composition. Students need to take into account the suitability of materials for their application and to consider volume manufacturing processes.

Commercially a number of designing and manufacturing constraints must be taken into account, e.g.

◆ the opacity of the paper if printing both sides so print does not show through
◆ the abrasive qualities of some papers wear out the printing plates too quickly in high volume printing
◆ web-fed printing (from a roll) seldom uses recycled paper because the fibres are chopped shorter than virgin paper and it is therefore more prone to breakage. This can be corrected by adding varnish or laminating, but these processes defeat the object of recycling

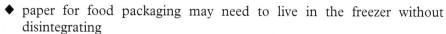

- paper for food packaging may need to live in the freezer without disintegrating
- recycled paper is not used for food packaging because the small traces of metal it contains are picked-up in quality checks that detect metal bits in the food.

Information technology in graphics and design

Computer graphics have been divided into two distinct types depending on their underlying technology: vector (object) and raster (bit-mapped). Both of these can be experienced by students in school. Vector graphics store information about objects by recording the position of the ends of lines, their length and angle, curves, fills, graduations etc. (See the packaging case study on page 50). Raster technology records an image on a pixel-by-pixel basis, each picture cell (pixel) being recorded as holding information or not. Further information can be stored in either technology such as texture and colour fills, although originally, vector graphics could only handle linework. These two technologies led to quite distinct developments in the use of computers in the design fields.

Vector graphics (object oriented)

Vector graphics led to computer-aided design drafting (CADD), the earliest form of computer-aided design to develop. As an imitation of technical drawings, which had themselves previously been very limited graphically, this was seen as of value in the engineering field from an early stage. Parametrics – retaining key geometry whilst altering various dimensions – further increased productivity as libraries of standard parts could be developed into new designs.

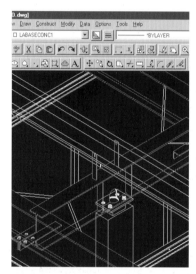

Standard steel sections joined to accommodate standard cladding materials.

A particular advantage of vector graphics (held as, for example, Postscript files) is the infinite level of detail they may contain. The design information is defined in terms of the relationship between lines, and therefore parts, or as a coded description of a fill. As you zoom-in so more and more detail becomes available, remaining true to the description of the object drawn. The output, in the form of plots or manufacture, can be at any level of detail or scale wanted. Vector graphics is described therefore as 'resolution independent'.

The engineering and architectural professions developed CADD capability fairly rapidly to include links to computer-aided manufacture (CAM) and sophisticated modelling procedures going beyond the basic geometry of the parts. These included the ability to specify the material that a part was to be made from and then to calculate its volume, weight, centre of gravity, concentrations of stress etc. Once a digital database of design information was generated, it could also be manipulated to produce such as the automatic generation of bills of materials. By this stage, it could truly be referred to as computer-aided design (CAD) – not just drafting.

Connecting to a wide area network allowed companies to link their designers across the world, which brought major advances in the time-to-market aspect of design development. These networks began to reach out across supply chains such that designers could source components from any company, anywhere and subsequently track their production, stock and delivery status. This is known as **electronic product definition (EPD)**.

TEACHER'S NOTES

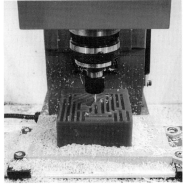

A student's CAD design being machined in a remote manufacturing centre.

Developments in CAD have been paralleled by CAM such that schools can now output CAD files direct to desktop manufacturing hardware for graphic products such as plotter-cutters and engravers.

Bit-maps

Raster graphics produce what is commonly called a bit-map – it maps the position of each bit of a drawing by pixel – so allowing any free-form shape, line, fill, colour depth etc. just as in vector graphics. By contrast with vector graphics, rasterised information is limited in detail to the resolution level it was created at. Zooming into (or enlarging the scale of) a drawing simply enlarges the sizes of the *bits* giving a chunky, unsatisfactory image (called '**pixellated**').

The Macintosh computer with its co-developed partner, desktop publishing software, brought to the graphic designer a CAD facility to parallel the engineer's in the mid 1980s allowing files of different types (initially text or graphics) to be imported into the DTP utility to make-up the desired page (hence the term page-make-up software). These might have been originated in another program such as a word processor or imported from a scanner, video or digital-stills camera. The stock-in-trade of graphic designers now, has become the combination of three types of program: Adobe Photoshop to manipulate photo images, Macromedia Freehand or Adobe Illustrator for drawing and text design, often combined in a desktop publishing package – Quark Xpress or Adobe Pagemaker.

The vast majority of professional graphic design is now carried out electronically which raises major questions for schools. Ignoring IT approaches is clearly no longer tolerable. However questions of equity of access are likely to remain. Nothing proves the imperative of allowing students to work beyond the capability of their teachers in Design and Technology than simply encouraging students to exploit IT based graphics to the full.

InSET: Developing computer graphics applications in your school

In preparation for this exercise, the session co-ordinator should, in advance, collect information and some examples of work showing which computer applications used throughout the school include some graphics capability – what they are used for, by whom and how much. Also, which applications specifically for graphics are available (e.g. Paint, Draw, CAD programs) – what they are used for, by whom and how much.

1 Preferably looking at the application on screen, or alternatively looking at output examples, assess their capabilities:

• Can drawings on the applications produce measured lengths of line that are accurate on outputs (e.g. print-outs)?
• Can they handle colour? Can you print in colour?

• Can they import images from input devices such as scanners, digital and video cameras?
• Can they manipulate images etc. downloaded from the Internet?
• How do their learning curves compare, i.e. which will be easy to start on and which will need training inputs?

2 Then discuss the potential for the applications you have looked at for use in your lessons. Identify where expertise lies (staff, students or others outside the school?).

3 Draft a development plan for this aspect of your work. Include sections on: research; teachers' skill development; student skill development; access arrangements.

What will students be expected to experience and achieve?

 D&T Routes
Teacher's Resource
for KS4, Turning a
syllabus into a
course, p31

Planning and maintaining a successful course in D&T Graphic Products needs considerable commitment from teaching staff even when using the different skills and abilities of all your team.

Summaries and mapping: developing an over-view of what you intend

A course map, or over-view, can assist greatly in keeping the teaching team together over time and between occasions when you meet to discuss the course in detail. While it would be inappropriate to predict all outcomes from a D&T course in advance of students starting work, it is helpful to map certain features well in advance. This can ensure coverage and enable efficient sharing of scarce resources, such as raw materials or systems and control facilities.

The level of detail that you decide to put into such mapping should be that which is most helpful to members of the team. While you may prefer to allow a flexible interpretation of the syllabus between teachers and teaching groups, care must be taken to avoid ambiguity and inconsistency. For example, the way in which students approach a particular aspect of the course may vary according to circumstance but the assessment and marking of their work should fit departmental policy and the grade descriptions of the examination board.

Planning aids may be provided by an examination board's hand-book. Even so, it is likely that you will need to devise your own grids or templates to facilitate this process.

Combining GCSE D&T and GNVQ Manufacturing

Scope exists to offer in parallel, GCSE D&T Graphic Products and GNVQ Manufacturing courses to their mutual beneift. However, to do this necessitates close study of their overlaps and differences. In comparing the NC D&T Order, GCSE syllabuses and GNVQ Manufacturing specifications you will find it helpful to home-in on particular themes to sharpen your ideas and help deepen your understanding of contemporary practices.

InSET: Comparing GCSE and GNVQ (Part One or full Intermediate)

Select a common theme, e.g. 'components, equipment and machinery and their preparation for manufacturing' and ask, what expectations are made of students on each course?

Use these questions to help you search for comparisons across syllabuses and specifications:

- what is meant by key characteristics and properties of materials required for the manufacture of given products?

- what preparation of materials for manufacture is specifically mentioned and how is it categorised?
- what processing methods are specifically mentioned?
- how specific to particular materials are these preparation and processing methods?
- how could you broaden the range of experiences for students in D&T Graphic Products to cater for greater understanding of industrial manufacturing?

TEACHER'S NOTES

With GCSE D&T and GNVQ Manufacturing being followed by members of the same class it is most important that teachers are clear about the similarities in and the differences between the syllabus or specification requirements. The accompanying grid has been drawn up to help with this.

GCSE D&T

		product	accuracy and reliability
2.2	Develop procedures for quality outcomes and safe practice	Accurate work to match scale of production and quality	Devise and use suitable checks for quality and reliability
2.3	Choose and use resources to make products effectively	Make a survival product	Use available tool and resources, evaluate production and products
3	Analysing products and applications	Case study at least two existing survival products	Assemble/disassemble products and critically evaluate them
4	Health and Safety	Features of products and manufacturing work practices	Safe workshop practice, safety standards, designing safe products
5	Quality	How quality determines reliability of survival products	Fitness for purpose in reliability, strength, environmental impact
	Materials and components	Processing resistant materials and components	Marking out, cutting, forming, shaping, using components
	Systems and control	Input, process, output and feedback as useful properties	Power transmission, controlling movement, using mechanisms

GNVQ Manufacturing (Intermediate) Part 1

C1	Prepare materials, components, equipment and machinery	Characteristics of materials, their processing and storage	Selecting materials for manufacturability
C2	Process materials and components	Processing materials to produce different products	Describe, in outline and detail, processing of different products
C3	Assemble and finish components to specification	Carrying out assembly and finishing of products	Compare contrasting products, their scales of production, QC, QA
C4	Apply quality assurance to manufactured products	Identify and use quality indicators during production	Testing and comparing at critical control points during production
GNVQ MANUFACTURING: Additional units for Full Intermediate award			
3.1	Produce production plans	Draw up plans for manufactured products	Scheduling and researching the stages of industrial production
3.2	Calculate the cost of a product	Estimating costs and working out price	Calculating costs for products of differing scales of production
3.3	Investigate quality assurance	Quality assurance investigated as a system	Describing and using quality control techniques for a product
KEY COMMUNICATION SKILLS			
2.1	Take part in discussions	Contribute to discussion with survival product audience	Discussion group: how climbers protection equipment works

InSET: Clear learning goals for students

In discussion with colleagues, complete and evaluate this exemplar route through a DMA which highlights *Application of quality assurance to manufactured products* (GNVQ Intermediate C4) and *Develop procedures for quality outcomes and safe practice* (GCSE 2.2).

The activity is based on the Survival DMA in this book and the pathway reveals common ground between the work in GCSE and GNVQ Manufacturing – developing checks for quality and reliability in their assignments. GCSE students may be deciding the level of accuracy needed for their product to work as intended. Manufacturing students may be deciding what kind of quality indicators are needed at what critical points in a production run.

Consider:

- what you want students to know and understand about quality
- in the light of this, what variety of experiences they need
- whether different resources are needed for different individuals
- whether tasks are open, encouraging autonomous learning, or closed
- how and when to check what students know.

Preparing additional resources to support DMAs

You will probably want to customise particular DMAs for use in your school. While the full and outline DMAs, used in conjunction with the Designing and Manufacturing sections of this book, provide a flexible framework for students, you can further extend their value by producing supplementary materials and worksheets of your own.

Systems and control in graphic products

You will find it useful to assemble a collection of graphic products that students can investigate including such as pop-up books, advertising products and greetings cards that incorporate flashing LEDs or sound effects.

Students could be asked to work out how systems and control have been used to achieve a function, what the system is doing, what makes it happen. Also, to analyse the inputs and outputs of the system, any processing that is used, what type of system it is and if any systems have been inter-connected to achieve the desired outcome.

Below is an example of an extension task to add-in to a DMA (in this case pop-ups) to provide differentiated work in systems and control for more able students. This provides an electronic sound effect circuit that would make noises when a pop-up was opened.

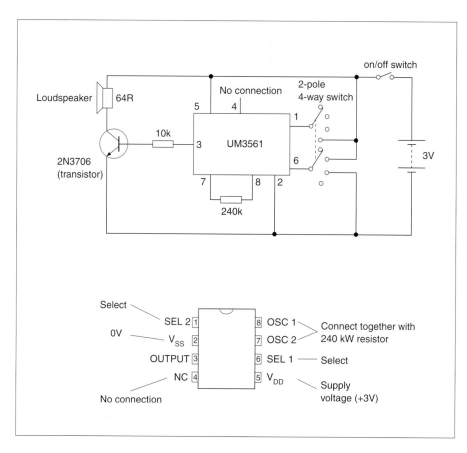

The UM3561 integrated circuit is a simple sound-effect generator which can produce three different sound effects – you can alter these by using the switch.

Print processes - reference chart

Name	Features	Uses
Screen printing	Limited to combinations of single colours, will print on almost any surface, limited detail possible, simple, economical, hand or machine methods used, relatively slow, most products printed after manufacture, economical for short runs (100 or less)	Signs, T-shirts, bottles, cartons, ring binders
Gravure	High setting-up costs, expensive cylinder plates, corrections difficult and expensive, excellent quality print, especially good for halftones and limited edition art prints, high speed/easy drying, good results on cheaper stock, excellent for long runs (millions)	Magazines and books
Letterpress	Good ink impression and colour, fine quality print, needs quality papers, expensive type and blocks, slow sheet-fed machines, little wastage	Card invitations, high quality private press work
Lithography (offset)	Exact water and ink balance required, quality halftones and photographs, hard to get dense colour, will take cheaper paper, expensive setting-up under 1000 copies, quick to get ready, fast to run on flat material	Most commercial printing, books, magazines, brochures, colour and high quality work
Web offset lithography	As for lithography above but higher speeds; folding, cutting, gluing, stitching and perforating can be included at the end of the process; paper is cheaper and is fed from reels rather than as individual sheets	As for lithography above plus very long run publications, direct mail
Ink jet	Low quality, slow, quiet, computer-controlled, needs the right paper absorbency, will print individual messages, can have multiple nozzles for printing a range of items at once	Addresses, personalising direct mail, coding documents, numbering tickets or products
Photocopying	Variable quality and speed, immediate results, unit cost is fixed, can collate, resize, sort, copy both sides, some can bind and side-stitch, can print up to 250 gsm hand fed	'On-demand' work, short runs and one-offs
Laser	Relatively slow, excellent quality, limited size, quiet and computer-controlled	High quality personalised items, letters or direct mail, short runs and one-off colour

Paper used for printing – reference chart

Name	Description	Weight	Where used
Bank	Lightweight bond	70 gsm or less	Carbon copies
Bond (woodfree*)	Fine white paper	80–120 gsm	General use stationery, writing, copying and magazine paper
Newsprint	Lowest grade of print paper, cheap, absorbent, discolours quickly	100 gsm approx.	Newspapers
Mechanical print	Superior newsprint, will discolour eventually	100 gsm approx.	Magazines, cheap leaflets
Cartridge	Closely woven, sized rougher surface, tough	100–135 gsm	Booklets, drawing paper, litho-printing
Antique	Textured or smooth surface, hand-finished look	100–135 gsm	Good for text, not for tone books, dust covers, brochures

*Woodfree is not really wood-free but chemically rather than mechanically treated.
It has strength, good colour and is usually used for better quality printing.

Coated papers – reference chart

Name	Description	Weight	Where used
Machine coated	Spray coated during manufacture, economical, good halftones	up to 160 gsm	Magazines, illustrated books and brochures
Cast coated	Machine coated extra heated finish, high polished/gloss finish	up to 160 gsm	Presentation covers, labels and packaging
Art paper	China clay coated gloss, matt or silk finish, high quality, extra smooth, good for halftones	up to 160 gsm	Magazines and promotional material
Board	Uncoated or coated can be laminated together to make thicker board	160 gsm upwards	Covers for paperbacks, catalogue covers and cartons
Art board	Covered with lining paper on both sides	160 gsm upwards	Packaging

Carbonless copying papers: the back of the top copy is coated with micro capsules of colourless dye solution. These are ruptured by the pressure of the printing or writing and the released solution reacts with the treated surface below to convert the dye to its colour.

Technical papers: highly specialised papers used for a wide variety of products such as currency, photography, filters, electrical cable winding, fancy laminates and postage stamps.

Plastic papers: made solely from plastic or plastic over a base paper. Expensive but good for maps, workshop manuals and children's books.

Glossary

Words in *italic* can be found elsewhere in the glossary.

Axonometric drawings show an object in 3D. The term extends to various standard forms of presentation, including *isometric*, *planometric* and *oblique*.

Bleed-proof paper is specially treated to prevent colours from spreading out and giving a blurred image. For example when using spirit markers.

Bond is the most commonly used plain paper in school. A thinner paper, known as **bank**, can be used as a semi-tracing paper because it is just thin enough to see through.

BS, short for **British Standards**, are conventions found in a standards manual, such as BS308 for drawing using rules. Drawings that conform to BS are easier for manufacturers to understand and help avoid mistakes during production. Increasingly BS incorporate International Standards (ISO) as well.

Calligraphy is the art of lettering produced by hand.

A **cam and follower** is a mechanism that provides a repeated movement.

Case may be UPPER (capitals) or lower (non-capitals) and is a term that applies to lettering style.

Clip-art is a computer library of images, each of which can be cut and pasted into other pieces of work when needed.

A **crate** is a type of construction grid used to assist free-hand drawing.

Copy (noun) is a term used for text-based information.

Copyright is the legal right to ownership of *copy* or artwork that cannot be copied for use without the originator's permission.

Dry transfer is a type of pre-formed, self-adhesive lettering.

DTP stands for **desktop publishing**: page make-up software that allows a graphic designer to combine a variety of text and images and to create a final *layout*.

Exploded drawings show all or some parts of a product, pulled apart to give more information about how hidden aspects and parts are assembled.

A **GA drawing** is used to show all parts of a product together in a **general arrangement**, usually in *orthographic* projection.

Ground is the surface on which you are working and may be either ready-made or specially prepared.

A **horizon** is an imaginary line at eye-level, used for perspective drawing, on which *vanishing points* are placed.

An **input** signal is energy put into a *system* or product.

Intaglio is a name given to printing methods where printing ink is held in grooves on the plates rather than on raised surfaces (as in *relief printing*).

Isometric is a form of *axonometric* drawing where horizontal lines are drawn at 30° and plan shapes are distorted.

Kerning is done to make detailed and often small changes to the spaces between letters, increasing or decreasing the width.

Layout is the way that text and images are arranged together in a designated space. It includes their position, size and orientation and how they work together.

Leading (*pron: 'ledding'*) is a typographer's term for a space between lines of type, increasing or decreasing its height. In past times strips of lead were used to create these spaces.

Lithography is a high-volume printing process which uses a water resist principle to control the quality of the printed image.

Moiré effect is blurring of an image caused by inaccurate lining up, or registration.

Oblique drawing is a form of *axonometric* drawing which shows one horizontal surface and one at an angle, usually 45°.

Orthographic means a straight-on view (with no perspective distortion). Orthographic projection usually shows several such views as though they were seen at 90° to each other to make-up one drawing.

Output is the term describing the effect of a *system* on the outside world.

Perspective drawings give an object a more realistic appearance by converging lines to a *vanishing point*.

Planometric drawings are true plans which have been given a realistic height.

A **print-run** is the number of copies to be printed from an original at any one time.

A **proof** is a realistic sample of a page *layout*, or other printed item, used for inspection prior to final printing. It is a printer's final **prototype**.

Points and **picas** are special units of measurement used for type.

A **pictorial drawing** shows an object in 3D, like a picture.

Primary colours, yellow, blue and red, are those that cannot be made by mixing other colours.

Process colours, black, cyan, magenta and yellow, are the four colours combined in a print-process to make full colour images.

Projection is a method of sending information from one part of a drawing to another.

Relief printing is a method that uses raised surfaces to transfer ink to paper.

Sectors of manufacturing are defined by the Confederation of British Industry to identify the contribution of products to the UK economy. Most graphic products belong within the Paper & Board, Print and Publishing sector.

Screen printing is a method of printing that uses a fine mesh or screen through which the printing ink is squeezed onto the product surface.

A **section** is a cut-away drawing showing internal details.

A **swatch** is a sample showing colour, texture, etc. (e.g. of fabric), used as a portable source to select from.

Systems have *inputs* and *outputs* and perform a clear function. They can often contain a number of smaller **sub-systems** each with its own inputs and outputs. A **system boundary** is used to define the limits of the system. **Systems diagrams** are used to represent systems.

Tolerance is the permissible allowance above or below the normal size of a component.

Total product costs are the sum of the prime costs (e.g. the materials used to make the product), production overheads (e.g. warehousing and transport), and non-production overheads (e.g. rent on premises, advertising etc.) and help to determine the **price** of the product.

Typography is the study and design of lettering styles.

A **vanishing point** is a fixed horizon-point on a *perspective* drawing where lines which are really parallel appear to meet.

Web-fed is the name given to printing onto a continuous roll of paper, rather than onto individual sheets or **sheet-fed**.

A **working drawing** is one containing all of the accurate information necessary to manufacture a part.